HOW TO MAKE VICTORIA SPONGE

Incorporating

A JEWEL IN THE SPONGE

© Margaret C M Kazmierczak 2014
ISBN 9781906631420

This edition published in 2014 by Arbentin Books Ltd
on behalf of Margaret C M Kazmierczak and printed in the UK.

Printed and bound in the UK by 4edge Limited, Essex

The author has asserted her rights under the Copyright, Designs and
Patent Act 1988 to be identified as the author of the work.

'What shall I do with Jesus who is called the Messiah?' This is a question we must all ask ourselves as God requires an answer. Our lives depend on that reply, and the response that we follow through with.

What shall I do with Jesus the Messiah? Shall I acknowledge him and just carry on, or shall I allow him into my personal life to save me from my sins?

Victoria Sponge is a fictional character who allows God into her life. Although there is tragedy and family issues constantly pulling at her time and efforts, she is able to offer each situation up to God. Her life becomes a constant prayer: a real part of her, not just a Sunday response. It matters not if she tells Him that she can't cope at a time of pain, because she has 'told' Him that. Therefore, even that message is a prayer. Through Victoria's prayer God shows her how His Holy Week is intertwined in her daily life. How He is in everything. Victoria Sponge might be fictional, but God's response is not.

Are we ready for that challenge to answer the question Pilate put to God's people? Are we prepared to allow God to be the secret ingredient in our mix? And are we ready to reveal what the secret ingredient is in our daily lives to others?

This book is dedicated to my family
with special thanks to Freda and Mike Bonard
as well as my wonderful friend Alison Angel
for all their help and encouragement

I am honoured that God chose me to write this book.

How to make a Victoria Sponge

1. Take one recipe book off the shelf and follow the instructions

2. Pop cake into the oven

3. Trust temperature and cooking skills

How to make Victoria Sponge

1. Take recipe book

2. Throw it in the bin

3. Trust God

Chapter One

Monday

Morning Prayer

'My sheep hear my voice, and I know them, and they follow me: And I give unto them eternal life; and they shall never perish, neither shall any man pluck them out of my hand. My Father, which gave them me, is greater than all; and no man is able to pluck them out of my Father's hand. I and my Father are one.'- Jesus of Nazareth; John 10:27-30

Monday, six fifteen in the morning and the alarm wakes me up for a new day.

My first words are 'Yes Father,' although I do not know the question.

Then I praise God for my husband Bob and my four children. Henry my eldest, Gabby and Johnny who are twins and lastly Lily Pink my youngest.

The day begins very quickly with a yell.

'Where's my school uniform?' Henry declares, 'Where's my PE kit?'

Of course the items are in the wardrobe, but for a teenager that is like saying they are on Mars. They don't see through doors and can only identify something if it is on their floor.

'Look in your wardrobe,' I suggest helpfully.

'It's not there,' Henry replies.

I wonder if he has actually looked and pop my head into his bedroom. Henry is still under the duvet.

Oh Lord, give me eyes that can see and ears that can hear. Give me a love that is patient, kind and tolerant.

I suggest that my son gets up and has another look, this time opening the door of the wardrobe. I dare not venture inside his room as it is a health and safety nightmare. First I might catch something and second I may end up in hospital having fallen over an object on the floor.

Oh Lord, please help me to keep to the straight and narrow road that you have prepared for me. But when I stumble and fall remind me to look where I am going!

I hear Henry yelling again, as I descend the stairs. He can't find his pants now. Then there is a rather large clonk.

'Oh that frigging drawer, why doesn't someone fix it?' he says frustratingly.

Oh Lord and carpenter, fix and heal those things in me that are troubling my soul and keeping me away from your presence.

From the commotion coming from Henry's bedroom the drawer sounds like it is being relocated, probably with all the contents still in it, to the other side of the room.

Oh Lord, may your peace descend on this household!

With the bacon spitting and the kettle steaming, toast popping up rather blacker than anyone likes it, I ask my husband, Bob to watch the breakfast cooking, and then I ascend to the room of another teenager. Dare I knock?

Oh Lord, give me courage in the face of tribulation and strife, help me to see beyond the darkness into the beauty that I know is residing somewhere behind this door.

I knock; will it be a good or bad day today? Nothing stirs. I sheepishly put on the light.

'Good morning dear' I say.

'I'm behind you mum' I hear. I jump out of my skin; Gabby is already awake and smiling. What a relief, it appears to be a good day. I sigh and say a thank you to the Father. Gabby is looking a picture of happiness.

Oh Lord, thank you for this moment of joy.

The smoke alarm starts to penetrate my being; its ear piercing wail puts my nerves on edge.

'Something's burning!' Bob yells.

I'm sure it is the bacon. When I return to the kitchen Bob is sitting at the computer not nursing the bacon, no wonder it is burnt. All that remains are charcoal remnants. Bob then leaves the computer and places a couple more slices into the frying pan and cooks up a meal that resembles an edible form.

Oh Lord, help me to rejoice for the help I receive however late it may be.

Back upstairs I trudge, two more little treasures to awake. I decide to check on Johnny first. He is still sleeping even though his alarm is trying its best to wake him up.

'Johnny,' I say quietly. Nothing.

'Johnny,' I repeat with a little bit more gusto, nothing again.

'JOHNNY'

I yell as loudly as I can. But still not a peep or any sign of movement, so I pull the duvet off his head. No wonder he can't hear me he still has his ear phones in.

Oh Lord, so often I am deaf to your calling, because I would rather do my own thing. Help me to listen to YOU.

Gabby enters her brother's room.

'Uh Johnny, your room stinks, open a window.'

She brushes past me and takes out his ear phones.

'It's half past eight, you are late.'

A bemused young man looks up at his sister; she must appear bleary without his glasses.

'Stop winding your brother up, it's not that late,' I say to my daughter.

She prances off to do her make-up and then all hell breaks out.

'No you can't borrow my make-up, go and use your own.' Lily Pink, Gabby's younger sister, says in an irate voice.

Oh Lord, so often I am late in talking to you about matters that concern me. I know that you don't mind being bothered about my needs and long to hear my requests. Help me to remember that we only have to ask and we shall receive.

Gabby and Lily Pink have an off/on relationship and today it seems it is an off one.

'Well thank you very much, I am going to be late now because I can't find my foundation,' she yells. The girls share a room which is divided by a curtain down the middle to give them each a little bit of privacy. Their make-up takes up most of the surface of their individual chests of drawers; however Gabby also uses her floor space too, the carpet having been ruined by spilt or trodden on remnants.

'All I want is a little bit, oh, you are so selfish,' she says.

This is not an argument that I want to be part of so I walk downstairs again and am handed a welcome cup of tea.

Oh Lord, it is easy to become argumentative and angry during the course of the day. Help me not to be selfish and distracted from focusing on YOU.

I believe that two elephants are descending the stairs as the racket is deafening.

'Mind the light,' the child's father reminds them as they jump the last four steps. Too late, there is a ping and the light blows as Henry head butts it out of the way.

Johnny is the first to the kitchen and picks up a plate with eggs and bacon on it. His hair is all over the place and it looks and smells like he did a spot lick, instead of having a shower.

Oh Lord, wash me clean from my sins and renew my flagging spirit.

'Thanks mum,' he says and opens the fridge. He downs a pint of milk in one go, and puts the empty bottle back. He then takes half a loaf of bread for his lunch and leaves for school.

'What about your sandwiches son?' my husband asks.

'I've got them,' he calls out, not realising that the half - loaf of bread was for the other sandwiches I need to make for the hungry mob that is left.

Oh Lord, give me wise words to feed my children with each day. Help me to point them to your LOVE and quench their thirst.

I quickly defrost another loaf of bread in the microwave. Henry meanwhile is bemoaning the fact that Johnny drank all the milk. I reassure him that the milkman will be here in a minute with enough for everyone. The telephone rings, it is Johnny; he has left his maths book at home. As soon as I put the phone down it rings again. Surprise, surprise it is my son again; he needs his science folder too. My husband and I search the possible places that might camouflage the two items but we find nothing. Gabby who has vacated the bathroom and ventured downstairs, holds up a wet plastic folder.

'Do you think Johnny needs this?' she asks. Thank the Lord it is the science project, not only is it wet but it is sticky with some sort of fluid all over it too, but at least it has been found. Unfortunately, the maths book is still elusive.

Oh Lord, thank you that you are not elusive. Help me to seek you and find you in all things, both great and small.

Gabby looks like a million dollars and much older than her fourteen years. My breath is taken away by her beauty. I am not sure if her make-up is part of the uniform, but she assures me that it is in compliance with the regulations. I suggest that she pulls her skirt down and she agrees to unroll it a fraction. Gabby doesn't do breakfast, but removes the empty bottle of milk that Johnny left in the fridge, has a cursory glance at the rest of the contents and then closes the door. Well I suppose she looked at the food. She stuffs her pocket with snacks for the bus ride and takes her sandwiches and drink. Gabby air kisses us both, takes Johnny's folder and departs for school. Henry, meanwhile, is still waiting for the milkman.

Oh Lord, you blow me away with your beautiful creation. You have painted a masterpiece from an empty canvas. Nothing is bland or ugly in YOUR vision, so help me to see everything through YOUR eyes today.

Johnny appears at the front door, he is worried about his maths book. He is almost in tears as he doesn't want a detention. We search the house again and then I search Johnny's rucksack. I find it in the front pocket looking more like a fly swat than a book. His relief is very apparent and he rushes off with a hasty 'Thank you'. He bumps into the milkman who drops our long awaited delivery. The milk smashes on the drive way and splatters all over our son's blazer and trousers. But Johnny just brushes himself down and runs as fast as he can to catch the bus.

Oh Lord, thank you for finding me when I was lost and alone. Help me never to lose sight of YOUR way.

Henry is now upstairs on his computer; he loves to cut everything fine.

'You are going to be late Henry,' I call out.

'I won't be long,' he calls down.

The front door bursts open, it is Johnny again.

'Where's Henry?' Johnny asks anxiously.

If Henry isn't on the bus with Johnny he panics. I am not sure what he will do when Henry leaves school and Johnny is left to do the journey with Gabby.

Oh Lord, often the road seems long and hard when we are frightened. Give me courage to walk the path you have chosen for me each day.

Henry swings down the dogleg stairs and picks up his school bag and I toss him his sandwich box and drink. He hugs his brother and tells him not to worry so much as they have plenty of time. They try to leave the house side by side, but the door isn't wide enough and once they sort out who is going first they slam the door behind them. From a distance I hear my husband's exasperated voice.

'Don't slam the ......'

Oh Lord, please protect my children as they start a new day. Help them to cope with the ups and downs of school life and support them in their friendship issues which will invariably challenge them today.

I hear a little voice coming from upstairs.

'Mum, I don't feel very well, can I stay at home today?' questions Lily Pink.

She has the shortest distance to go to school as she is in the last year of primary education. It is just a short walk away and Lily Pink usually makes the trip with some of her friends each morning. I take a look at her face, her tongue, feel her temperature and generally use a sympathetic tone stating that she will be much better at school if she makes the effort.

'But my tummy hurts,' she pleads. I sigh, but don't give in, as I have to go to work today.

'Please,' she whines. I stand firm and help her to get dressed. At 10 she is perfectly able to do this herself, but she likes the fuss and decides that perhaps she can struggle in today after all. She gives me a hug and a kiss and says that she will be alright now.

Oh Lord, bless my youngest child and help her to be brave in all that she does. Thank you for her smiles and cuddles that light up her face and make me feel warm inside and remind me of your loving gaze as you watch and care for us in our daily lives.

There is a commotion downstairs, rushing of feet, a yell of 'where's my keys?' and the door slamming again. I look out of the bedroom window and see my husband with Henry and Johnny. They obviously missed the bus so need a lift into school. I look at Lily Pink and think how pretty her blonde curly hair is. She is so different from the others, she has brown eyes and an olive toned skin. I am not sure who she takes after, perhaps she is an off shoot from a distant relative.

Oh Lord, thank you that we are all unique.

Lily Pink has a hearty breakfast of bacon, sausage and egg washed down with fruit juice. So maybe her tummy ache is better now! She packs her own bag and gives me instructions as to what she wants in her lunch box. All sorted she messages her friend to say that she is ready. Her thumbs travel over the key pad at an alarming rate and then stops for a second before answering another message from another friend. I am beginning to wonder if we will evolve into a thumb only race. I mean what do you need the other fingers for?

Oh Lord, I am not sure how we keep up with all the technology that floods our market place. Thank God that you are consistent and we can rely on your presence in an ever changing world.

The doorbell rings –

'Don't worry mum, I'll get it as it is bound to be for me!'

My daughter has a better social life than I do! But it is good to see her happy and excited about life. My shoulders relax at the thought that I have managed to complete the first phase of the day without too much hassle. Now it is my turn. Shower, get dressed, breakfast, teeth, lippy and prepare bag. The bathroom is strewn with wet, soaking towels thrown on the floor. Shampoo drips from its container into the bath and the soap is sliding around precariously close to my foot which is about to step in to the shower. I have let the water run for a little while to warm up. As I think about the delights of washing away the stress of this morning's preschool antics, I step under the shower head. IT IS COLD. I jump back out of the way shaking with the shock of being drenched by such a stark realisation that my family have left me with no hot water. I grind my teeth in frustration and mutter impure thoughts about each of my offspring. 'Aaaaaaaaah.'

Oh Lord, I understand that the first shall be last and the last shall be first. But could you organise a warm shower for me just for once. I have served my family this morning and the least I ask for is a little bit of consideration. You said ask and you shall receive, well I am asking for a shower with hot water. It's not much!

I do a quick over the body flit with a kettle of boiled water into the wash basin. Spray lots of all-purpose smelly all over, smudge some lipstick on and throw a few things into my bag. I forget to have some breakfast and open the door to the outside world. Oh great, God is having some fun because it is pouring down with rain. By the time I walk to work I will have had a shower. And who said God doesn't have a sense of humour!

And as I walk in the rain God says:

Vicki your prayer today was 'Yes Father', even though you didn't know what the question was. My dear daughter you have been holy this morning through your service to your family. Be blessed by my outpouring of the Holy Spirit into your everyday situations.

Eight forty five and the team are nearly ready to open the doors to the preschool where I work. There is a bubbly atmosphere and the fact that we work in a church building helps us to focus on our service to the children in our care.

Oh Lord and teacher, help me to be open to the needs of the children today. May our

15

enthusiasm rub off onto the children so that they can believe that they can attempt anything that we have prepared for them or they initiate for themselves.

As the doors open there are eager faces from both the children and the adults. The young ones run in and some put their coats on their pegs and others just throw them at the hooks. The parents follow by picking up their child's coat or nipping out quickly after their charge into the main room. All ready for the action, some have found the activities and start building, climbing or enthusiastically greeting friends they haven't seen since their last session. With the image of a happy child resting calmly on their hearts, the adult leaves content that all is well and they say their goodbyes. Some children are too absorbed in their world to say goodbye.

There is one child who refuses to leave their parent and starts to become hysterical. I gently encourage her mother to walk away and look through the glass door from the hall way. I create a distraction for the little one and after a few screams of 'I want my mummy,' she slowly looks around to see what the other children are doing.

Oh Lord, sometimes leaving my comfort zone is very scary and I would rather not make that move. I might have a tantrum or thrash about, pushing against the idea. When this occurs Lord, help me to be brave and take your hand knowing that you would never lead me to some place that I cannot cope with.

When all the children have arrived we sit them down on the floor and the manager tells them about the exciting morning ahead of them. The team have already been allocated their duties so everyone knows the general run of the morning's session. I get to do the creative stuff and toilet duty!

Oh Lord, if only my day was written down in a book with easy instructions of what and where to do and go, life would be so much easier. Instead my world is crazy and confusing most of the time. Grant me the flexibility and patience to cope with all the dramas each day presents to me.

My remit is the Art Room today, making bubble pictures. I sit ready with a straw in hand waiting for my first three year old to appear. But instead of one keen pre-schooler, four arrive at once eager to get paint

16

all over them. One dives straight in not wanting to hear instructions, another asks for help with their apron, the next starts drinking the paint through the straw and the last just stands there watching, looking very hesitant. I deal with the paint drinker and get the first child to put on an apron otherwise he will be covered in red, blue, green and yellow before he finishes his masterpiece. Then I gently encourage the little girl who doesn't appear to want to join in. I take a piece of paper and blow red paint onto it, then accidentally slip with the paint and end up with a blob on my face. She laughs, thinking this is very funny and slowly applies her own finger which she coats in yellow and draws on my face. The ice is broken and before you know it the shy eyes have gone and a beautiful picture covered in bubbles produced. My little student is delighted with her efforts.

Oh Lord and artist, how overjoyed you must be when we overcome our fears and try to bring colour into our lives. Help me to mirror your beauty to others through the gifts you have given me.

A teenager on work experience joins me and figures that I am not in control of the children's play, so she suggests kindly that I might like to go to the toilets and clean myself up! Several more children arrive in the room who don't want to get their hands messy. This time the children and I decide to produce a collage which, of course, involves me first getting my hands painted. Eagerly the group slop the colours over my outstretched hands. At this point a preschool assistant pops her head into the room and laughs at the state I am in. Surprised at the reaction of another adult to my chaotic condition the children realise that it is okay to have messy hands, so the aspiring artists get stuck in. They make swirls and blend colours on a large sheet of paper, dotting hand prints in any empty spaces. My teenage shadow decides after a while that perhaps getting down to the nub of the problem means that a hand on approach can reap many rewards.

Oh Lord, help me not to prejudge a situation before I have the whole facts. Help me to be humble in my opinions and generous in listening.

With the art session over the room has to be cleaned up for snack time. Paint is wiped off all surfaces, including my face and hands; with pots, straws and other items taken out for washing. The tables are put together to form little areas for socialisation and eating. When all is ready, the children are seated and we show them how to pass and share the fruit with each other. Some little ones like to dominate while others sit and survey the proceedings. Drinks are handed out and a general noise of chomping, slurping and plate moving fills the air. All is relaxed until someone spills their drink. Chairs scrape, shrieks are emitted from other children, tears flow, cloths appear to mop up the fluid, and wet clothes are replaced with dry, clean ones - quick, calm, efficient, loving.

Oh Lord of Calmness, when storms gather and life seems to take on a wobble or two, enable me to stay grounded and firm in your power.

With snack time over, the children are taken outside to let off some steam. There are scooters, trikes, and little cars, push chairs with dolls in them, a playhouse and a climbing frame, all manner of things to keep the young mind happy and occupied. Meanwhile I am in doors changing the pull-ups of a lad that doesn't want to wear another one. I try him on the potty and he sits happily doing nothing. After he says he has finished, and with some coaxing I achieve the job of putting a clean pull up on, only to see the little boy going red in the face and pushing very hard!

Oh Lord, mess happens. Give me strength.

I strip him down, trying to keep him distracted with 'Humpty Dumpty sat on the wall' smiling as I sing. He chuckles, is it my singing or the fact that he has given me a present to clean up?!

Oh Lord, how many times have you had to clean up after me? Thank you for your patience and love.

Having finished this service, I take the little boy outside where he instantly rushes around feeling free and at peace with his world. It is truly amazing to see children with arms outstretched embracing their world. No worries, just enjoyment of the present. We can learn so much from these young ones.

Oh Lord, you said, 'Bring me the little children,' and 'unless you become like children…' Help me to see and trust you by embracing the simplicity of a child's view, uncomplicated and pure.

With outdoor play over, we head back indoors where we get the parachute out. There is a lot of excitement as the children love this activity. The rules are explained as usual for their safety and an adult stands next to the smallest girl to make sure that her feet stay firmly on the ground when the parachute is in full flight! Hindsight is a wonderful thing! I cannot help but smile and laugh at the little faces as they ooh and ahh at the rising and falling of the piece of material. After a bit we let the youngsters go under it and lie down while we shake it vigorously over them. There are shrieks and screams of delight, their trust in us complete. They emerge with hair standing on end and an excited cry of 'again, again!'

Oh Lord, help me to fly with you through the winds of enjoyment that come unexpectedly during the day. Help me to catch these sudden air currents when they present themselves and use them to glide me into your presence.

We let the children have another go under the parachute and then play a little game with them to see if they know each other's names. When the parachute goes up two names are called out and the two children have to swap places. Davy looks bemused as Lucy heads for his place. He doesn't want to move and she wants his handle. He pushes her and she falls down, tears well up from Lucy and Davy just looks at her. He doesn't understand what the commotion is all about and runs off.

Oh Lord, it is so easy for me to misunderstand other people and to feel hurt by their actions. Please heal my lack of understanding and help me to discern their true intentions.

An assistant leaves the parachute activity and sits down close to Davy. He is standing with his arms folded and tapping his foot. He is confused and angry by the situation that has just occurred. He doesn't want to hear about his actions and closes down his receptors. My colleague is gentle and compassionate towards him and diverts his attention by bringing out a little puppet from her pocket. She talks to the puppet and uses it to talk about being kind to other children. Davy slowly unfolds his arms and makes a request to see the puppet. He talks to it, vents his anger at what has happened and then punches it several times before throwing it away. He is a lot calmer now and moves towards the assistant laying his head in her lap and closing his eyes.

19

Oh Lord, sometimes a problem seems too large for me to handle when I cannot see a solution. When this happens help me to rest my head in your lap knowing that you are the answer to everything and can bring healing and solace during these times.

The fun with the parachute is nearly over and Becky, the manager of the preschool, suggests that an adult crawls under the colourful material. The children are allowed to choose who. A chant goes up and it appears that it is me who they want for this treat. I get down on my hands and knees and crawl into the middle of the parachute. As the swishing and laughter grows louder the air underneath builds up and it sounds like there is a storm brewing above me. The parachute goes up and down and side to side wriggling over my body. It is a funny sensation knowing that you have no control over what is happening. By the time it all stops I am completely blown away and my hair is standing on end. I must look a state but the children all think it very funny. When the parachute is folded up and put away, some of them come over and give me a hug and tell me how funny I looked when I emerged from the experience.

Oh Lord, thank you that I am able to laugh at myself, even when it puts me in a vulnerable situation controlled by others. Help me never to lose that trust in YOU knowing that you always have my best interests at heart, and are in control of my life even when I am not.

We sit the children down for a quiet time with a story. As I make myself comfortable on the floor, several children come and lounge on me with big smiles. Everyone loves story time. What will it be about today? Oh, it is my favourite, 'We're going on a bear hunt'. The children join in with the verse that runs through the book, 'you can't go over it, you can't go under it…' It is a wonderful end to a fun filled morning. As the mums, dads, grandparents and carers begin to filter in to collect their charges, we see the excited faces on the little ones as they scan through the expectant faces looking for a familiar smile. They run to their adult with outstretch arms and full of news about their morning. One child hugs her mum and then decides she has forgotten something, she turns and looks at me and rushes back to give me a thank you cuddle, a perfect end to a morning full of service.

Oh Lord, how you delight when I rush to you with all my news whether it is good, bad, celebrating or complaining. You love to hear all about my day. Thank you for always being available when I need to share.

But this is not quite the end of the session for the rest of us, who have to tidy away all the efforts of the day. All the outside toys need to be stored in their shed and the indoor toys stacked neatly away in cupboards for another day. The floor needs to be hoovered and records written up. I share with the other members the highlight of my art morning and they talk about their experiences. We eat chocolate and relax, happy to be in one another's company. The team is supportive and challenging towards each other. I enjoy their company and the time spent in this way. It is a different kind of busyness in my life as it is not in the confines of my home. I can leave it behind me at the end of the morning, hoovered and clean, and find it in that state the next day! It is an atmosphere of sharing with everyone helping, supporting and carrying the load together.

Oh Lord, thank you that you see me for whom I really am. You see the beauty and the warts and you still love me. Even though I hoover on the outside there is so much to spring clean on the inside; but You are gentle and kind, encouraging and compassionate, patient and challenging, always prepared to support me when it is time to spring clean.

And God said:

Vicki, you have delighted me all morning with your smile and laughter, what a wonderful daughter you are. I am so proud of you. Thank you for bringing me to work with you today. For some people the only Bible that they see or read is you.

Afternoon Prayer

One o'clock and with the morning over I head back home. I love the walk back as I listen to the sound of nature talking to the world around it. Trees rustling, birds singing, a dog barking in the distance, clouds moving gently in the sky over head, shadowing the sun one moment then allowing it to erupt into a glorious spray of light the next. I realise how hungry I am having not eaten any breakfast. A growl rises in my stomach competing with a wood pecker close by. Then I slip on something not very nice. A present left by an animal whose owner hasn't cleaned it up. Great! A sudden call back down to earth and it smells. I cuss under my breath and then try to clean it off on the grassy area that surrounds the estate I am walking through. Most of the muck is scraped away but I realise that the rest will have to be sorted out when I get home.

Oh Lord, why are some people thoughtless and too busy to clean up after their animals?

It doesn't take long to get home and I find a parcel awaiting me behind the flower pot. This I pick up and put under the arm that is holding my bag and attempt to unlock my front door. It appears to be open. I kick off my poo shoe and leave it outside, stride indoors and promptly fall over a bag, hit my head on the vacuum cleaner that has been left out in the hallway, and activate the 'on' switch. As I vent my anger in various colours of blue, the noise of the vacuum drowns out the contents of my mouth and a head pops around the corner. It yells at me and asks if I am alright. In my head I respond, 'Do I look alright?' and heave myself up off the floor. The parcel is bent and my head hurts. There is an indentation of the on button protruding from a bump left on my forehead.

Oh Lord of today, thank you for the challenges you have sent me so far. Do you think you could rewire my husband's brain to remember not to leave his bag in the middle of the floor? Oh and forgive my swearing but I was in a lot of pain. I am sorry.

I look at my husband in a quizzical way. 'What are you doing home? I ask.

He responds by saying that he has taken a half day off to spend some time with me. I feel very dizzy and lean up against the wall my hand on my forehead. I ask for a wet towel which Bob attempts to get. He asks should he use a clean or dirty one! Preferably clean I say as I don't want to get germs mixed in if there is a cut. He stands in the middle of the kitchen and asks for a clue as to where they might be. I am beginning to feel that it would be easier if I just found one, but my legs are feeling funny, my head starting to throb and I need to sit down.

Oh Lord, sometimes I do not see what is in front of me. I look in the wrong direction and stand unsure of what to do, awaiting instructions from another source. Help me Lord to lean on YOU.

The world is beginning to go round in circles and I feel sick. Bob tries to lift me up as he thinks that I need to go to the Accident and Emergency Clinic on the other side of town. He realises that perhaps I am a little too heavy for him so he rings up the hospital instead. They advise him on concussion and what best to do. I figure the best place for me is bed, so I crawl up the stairs and get under the duvet. Bob appears asking where the towels are and I point to the airing cupboard just outside our bedroom. He comes in a few moments later with a dripping towel. I suggest that it might be better if it is a little less wet. Bob returns and places the cool cloth onto my head and I begin to relax. Bang goes our afternoon together doing something without the kids.

Oh Lord, how glorious it is to rest in your presence even though this moment was not planned. You know how painful a head injury is, having worn a crown of thorns. My pain is nothing compared to yours, thank you for bearing your pain for me.

Bob is still concerned about the bump on my head and after I have had a sleep he encourages me to go to the hospital. I manage to get down stairs and into the car, still holding my towel which has been rewetted. It doesn't take long to get to the A & E department and with it being a small cottage hospital we don't have too long to wait for a nurse to assess me. She just confirms what the person had told Bob earlier on in the afternoon about concussion and gives me two tablets for the headache. However, she emphasises that I ought to rest and take it easy the rest of the day. Chance would be a fine thing. Reassured, Bob thanks the nurse and we leave the hospital. Back in the car Bob comments that at least we have got out for a little bit!

Oh Lord, you said that when we are old we would be taken to places that we would rather not go, well the hospital was one of them for me. Bless Bob for his concern for me, but perhaps next time you could arrange a trip to, oh gosh where is that place again with lots of water?

My memory is troubling me, I am feeling really tired again and I want to burst in to tears. It must be the concussion. Sitting next to me Bob is getting frustrated because someone has parked right across the back of our car, leaving us stuck in the hospital car park. He gets out and walks around the car to see if there is any way he can manoeuvre around it, but there is simply no way he can do so. He looks around trying to conjure up the driver of the car, but no one is around. The front windscreen has a disability label on it, which annoys Bob as the parking space for the disabled drivers is across the way unoccupied. Bob sighs and decides to go for a walk to see if he can find someone to help sort the situation out.

Oh Lord, my head is throbbing, I feel confused and unwell, please fix this situation for me soon. I would like nothing better than to be at home in bed. Thank You for hearing my prayer.

Bob returns fairly quickly with a gentleman who is apologising profusely about having parked in such an awkward manner for us. His mother has been rushed to hospital and he was so worried about her that he wasn't thinking straight when he parked. He gets into his car and reverses slowly, turns left narrowly missing the end car and then moves forward. His battery decides to die at precisely this moment. He raises his hands to heaven and bangs them on the steering wheel.

'She's died, I know she has." The gentleman gets out of the car and murmurs.

Bob thinks he means the car, so he suggests that he help push it into the spot for the disabled. The man walks off leaving Bob to finish the job of parking it, which he does by pushing and steering at the same time. He has to jump in quickly to grab the hand brake in order to stop the car in its tracks. This done, Bob takes out the car keys, shuts and locks the door then follows where the gentleman has gone. He returns a little later with the news that the mother has indeed died. He had also kindly given the man our phone number in case he needs a lift later as his car is incapacitated.

Oh Lord, am I ready for a shocking moment? How will I receive it when it comes? Will there be a friendly person to help me through it? Please Father, when this happens to me grant me the ability to cope and the sense to call on YOU.

As Bob turns into our drive way, Lily Pink is waiting for us at the front door. She doesn't have a key as I am usually at home when she arrives in the afternoon. She looks quizzically at me wondering what is going on. I show her my forehead with the bump on it and she commiserates with me, taking my hand and leading me carefully inside the house as she walks backwards. She falls over the same bag I did but misses the hoover. I tell her that that is what I did. She picks herself up and throws her dad's bag to one side and tells him off for leaving it in the middle of the floor. I look at Bob and he mouths 'Sorry'. Lily Pink then piles her school bag on top of her father's. She leads me upstairs and tells me to get changed and to go to bed. I am then told not to worry as she will take care of things for me.

Oh Lord, thank you for the kind nature that you have bestowed upon my youngest child. I am not sure if I can settle without worrying, as leaving everything to a 10 year old is a big commitment of trust. Help me with this choice Father.

Everything appears to be quiet downstairs, and I gently drift off in a shallow sleep. It feels like only a moment ago that I closed my eyes when the front door opens and there is a lot of banging and crashing. I can hear Johnny's voice stressing over where the school bags should be put, Gabby asking who left their coat on the hall floor, and whose shoe is discarded on the stair and Henry yelling in an annoyed way over who had had the last Snickers bar. There is stomping up the stairs, a 'Hi mum, heard you hit your head or something, it's alright you don't have to get up, we will be fine,' through the door and then music, loud music, in fact not just loud music but deafening music. The bass sound of the music is competing with the thudding of my headache. Lily Pink opens my door and lets in the full force of the pulsating noise. I look at her in agony and she closes the door. The music stops just like that and voices are raised.

'You can't just pull out the plug you little monster.'

'But mum has a headache.'

Henry loves his music, and Lily Pink was fortunate not to be hung, drawn and quartered for messing with his sound system. There is a sigh.

'OK, I'll put my earphones on,' Henry states.

The door closes and Lily Pink puts her head around my door. 'I told you I would take care of things!'

Oh Lord, if only things were as easy as that normally. How good it would be to be able to just switch things off that I don't like about myself. My jealousy, my impatience, my anger all gone at a flip of a switch. But You know that each of these impurities is a chance for growth, for my growth. Help me Father, to grasp these opportunities when they arise.

A raised voice echoes through the house.

'Oh I don't believe it, you silly animal. I know you are hungry, just hang on a moment I can't do everything.'

I am not sure if Bob is talking to the cat or to one of the children. Gabby joins the conversation trying to be heard as things clatter on the kitchen floor. She doesn't like chips, doesn't want pie, won't eat fish, is fed up of mince and why can't she just go and get something from the Chinese? She storms off in a rage and heads for her bedroom. She tries to slam the door but Bob has put a stopper on the top of it to prevent such a happening. This makes Gabby even more cross. I hear something about 'hate house, people in it and jerks.'

Oh Lord, thank God we are not jerks in your eyes. We may be a mystery to one another but comprehending our nature is a life long journey. I am so grateful that you are the Map I can refer to when my view is hindered by my emotions.

I expect Bob is on the computer letting Johnny and Lily Pink deal with the tea having fed the cat. The smoke alarm goes of.

A little smile appears and says, 'Don't worry mum, it is only Johnny burning the beef burgers, we won't waste anything as he will scrape off the burnt bits!'

The alarm shuts off after someone starts waving a towel at it; how do I figure this from my bedroom? Well, the light is already broken so another swipe to it does little damage, which means some form of floppy material is used to quieten the smoke alarm and has also hit the hall light shade, making it swing and hit the ceiling after the alarm has been silenced. It must be Lily Pink as she is short and needs a longer thing to sweep through the air to dispel the invisible smoke. So I was right about Johnny and L P doing the tea.

Oh Lord, you never waste anything, knowing that everything is part of the bigger picture. With You all things can be used to a greater benefit and even when I ruin the plan You are able to turn it around for Your honour and glory. Praise God.

No sooner has the alarm stopped than a new chapter starts, and it sounds like someone is in trouble downstairs. A little head pops round my door again.

'Johnny has burnt himself mum,' Lily Pink yells.

I tell her that I will be down in a moment. She argues and says that I must stay in bed, but I know Johnny, he will be panicking and in pain unable to help himself with his injury. I slowly arise, I feel unsteady but an internal power takes over and I move knowing that I need to get downstairs. The kitchen is full of smoke.

'Don't open the door!' Bob calls out. Silly really as I can't get in unless I open the door. Naturally the alarm is triggered. Johnny is holding his hand and trying to be brave, hopping around in a limited space where the cooker door is flat open as the grill is an internal one. I have always hated that style, thinking it a fatal flaw offering a trip trap. Not good, someone else could get hurt. Bob has taken over the cooking. I have no choice but to try and cram Johnny and myself over the sink to run cold water over his left hand. His wails are understandable as it hurts.

Oh Lord, calmer of commotions, bring peace to this storm in my kitchen. Heal my son's hand and let there be no scar from the burn he has suffered. Thank you that he wanted to help me, please now help him.

Henry appears at the kitchen door.

'Don't open the door,' shouts Bob.

'What's for tea,' his son asks.

Bob glares at him and he shuts the door. Henry does what is the most sensible thing so far; he finds a stepping stool and takes out the battery of the fire alarm. The piercing wail has stopped and Henry re-enters the kitchen. We all chorus 'thank you', and Bob reminds his son to put the battery back in later. Now there are five of us in the room. Bob shoos Lily Pink and Henry into the dining room and asks them to lay the table. Of course that means that they have to come back into the kitchen to get the knives, forks, and glasses. There is a lot of movement and side stepping. Bob dishes up, the burgers in a bap with chips and a salad. Meanwhile I continue to keep Johnny's hand under the tap until I am satisfied that it has had enough cold water on it. I tell him that if it starts to throb to run it under the cold tap, emphasizing the cold as he might use the hot one instead.

Oh Lord, how grateful I am that you are not battery operated. What would I do if I called on you and you were disconnected or being recharged and out of commission? It is so comforting that you are always close.

Food usually takes Johnny's mind of most things, and I am heartened to see him woofing down his tea. Gabby had joined us and eaten her fill. She takes off again as quickly as possible because she is waiting for a reply from a friend on her mobile phone. I try my best to eat the generous portion Bob has given me but my stomach doesn't seem to be in much of a mood for what is on my plate. It doesn't take a lot of coaxing from the family for me to return to my bed. Suddenly Bob is left on his own with all the washing up. It is amazing how four children can become invisible so quickly.

Oh Lord, how often do I do things so quickly that I don't appreciate the effort others have taken to create something. Sometimes I forget even to say thank you and rush off to my chosen activity forgetting that a simple thank you can be so uplifting to the person receiving it. Help me be mindful of this Father.

I hear Bob calling all four of our children; he is not going to let them get away with not helping with the washing up.

Oh Lord, how often do I try and get away with not doing a chore? Help me not to forget that you are in the chores as well as in the important tasks of life.

And as I lay in bed God speaks to me:

My dear Vicki, just as I created everything on this earth for a purpose, I have given you this family for a reason. Step back with me and look at the fruits of your efforts this afternoon. Although you fell under your cross, you stood up. That takes courage, my daughter, you are very courageous.

Evening Prayer

As I am resting Bob comes up and tells me what had happened earlier with the washing up. He comments that Gabby had been the first down saying that she would wash up the dishes if he did the pots. He said that he had agreed and thanked Gabby as she was trying to be helpful. I was very pleased that Gabby had made this effort; she was usually the one to come last when most of the chores had been done. Henry had put the battery back into the smoke alarm and had asked if Johnny could be excused as his hand still hurt. Gabby had wrapped a wet cloth around the scalded area, and had told Johnny to keep the cloth wet as it would help with the pain. Then Lily Pink had rushed in and grabbed a dish cloth. Henry and L P had started a cloth fight and Gabby chastised them as she had wanted to get the washing up done as quickly as possible. In the end Bob said that he had stopped the antics and taken over from Gabby as she had done her share. Henry and Lily Pink had finished drying and offered to put everything away. So miracles do happen I think to myself.

Oh Lord, it is good to celebrate the positive attempts that our children make as and when they occur. I am guilty of forgetting those moments at times. It seems far easier to remember and comment on the negatives. Dear Father, turn this action upside down so that I may empower my family with my remarks during the day.

I can see that Bob is tired but he knows that there is still homework to contend with. Gabby will have got on with hers asking for help from friends on her mobile. So as she says, it is helpful to have 24/7 connection. We don't really see Gabby in the evening apart from meal times. I am not even sure what time she goes to bed as she sorts all of that out herself. There is not usually a 'goodnight' to define the bedtime hour. But we have come to trust that she is in bed at a reasonable time. This has been a compromise as she felt she needed some responsibility. So if she is exhausted the next day she knows why. Fortunately Lily Pink can sleep with the light on in Gabby's area of the room and doesn't need to be told when to go to bed as she is flat out by eight thirty.

Oh Lord, thank you that you have given me free will. What a range of choices I have, to believe or not to believe, to be free or not to be free, to hide or to walk openly, to embrace or not to embrace my life. The choices are endless but not without signposts or consequences. My choice, help me to make the right ones.

Bob looks in on Henry, he is reading a book.

'Have you any homework?' he says.

'Uh yeah, I'll do it in a minute," is the reply.

Lily Pink storms in to our room and does a roly poly on the bed; she has arrived!

'I've got homework to do,' she says. She snuggles up and puts my arm around her.

'Is this your homework?' I tease her. She giggles, jumps off the bed, down the stairs and back again in record time.

'No this is!' and she slings her bag on to the bed and settles under my arm again, safe and secure.

Oh Lord, how wonderful it is to feel safe and secure in Your arms, no matter what I have done, even though I am a sinner, in your eyes I am as beautiful today as the day I was born. What an awesome thought. How great is your LOVE.

I think our bedroom is open house, as Johnny decides that he can't do his homework with a poorly hand, especially as he is left handed. Henry also appears and sprawls out on the bed. Then Bob makes an appearance, and if Gabby arrives too it will be a full house. Like bees to a honey pot. With so much jocular behaviour Gabby does enter the room and join us. She surveys the bodies and hurls herself towards a vacant space, right near my legs which I manage to pull up just in time. It is a moment of madness with limbs all over the place. I don't want to break up the fun as it has been awhile since we all played like this. Then the tickling starts and Bob is ambushed by all four offspring. They take off his slippers and pull open his shirt. He begs for mercy but they are hysterical. Finally Henry falls off the bed and narrowly misses falling on the cat. Then everything becomes calm again.

Oh Lord, this joy makes my heart bubble over as I see the different characters of one family merged together to form an unbreakable bond. Is this what the Trinity is like? One, but different entities making a greater Whole. Making it complete? If this is what makes family holy, help me Father to keep us united and whole. Holy in your Trinity.

I look at my motley crew and sigh. There's short fair curly hair, long dark hair, long fair curly hair and straight short dark hair. There are brown and blue eyes, pale and olive skin. Not to mention the grey receding hair line and the brown fighting the grey curly hair of Bob and I. All different but all from the same batch. Bob looks for his slippers and puts on his deep father voice.

'Homework now!' The moment is broken and heads hang low. Back to reality.

Oh Lord, when I get to heaven will there be homework or will I know everything? Will my questions be answered or will I even remember what questions I wanted answered? In your light will these things be important or will I just be?

Gabby leaves first, I call her name and she looks back, she is so beautiful, I say thank you to her for helping her father with the dishes and she smiles at me. I long to be able to cuddle her again, like I did before she became a teenager. But I know that everything these days is on her terms, and when she is ready she will approach me. Her world is full of contradictions and embarrassment especially with Bob and me. She wants us but she doesn't, so we just try and merge with the background, ready for when Gabby needs us. I know that her door to us is closed at the moment, but the phase will pass and we will be able to knock again and be invited in.

Oh Lord, thank you for the amount of times that you have waited for me to open my closed heart to you. That you have never given up on me. How loyal you are to me, a wayward spirit. How unconditional your LOVE.

Henry lingers but only because something is on his mind, Johnny asks Bob to go over a French problem with him and they go to the dining room. Lily Pink meanwhile starts to take out her homework from her school bag and realises that she needs to use the computer to access her science revision. With L P gone and Henry now alone with me he gets up and closes the door. Being in bed seems a popular place to be. I am accessible whether I like it or not. Henry, my 16 year old with short dark hair and brown eyes, is chewing over his problem in his head before forming it into words.

'There's this girl I like,' he starts, 'and I am not sure if she likes me.'

He looks at me waiting for a reaction, he hasn't mentioned girls before. He's not really been that interested, having two sisters, which no doubt put him off before now.

'I think you would like her.' He seems embarrassed and wanting approval, I remark that I am sure any girl he chose would be lovely because he was a kind and caring lad. Then the crunch question comes.

'How do I ask her out?'

I respond with a simple answer. 'Just ask her face to face if you can.'

He thinks about this.

'Can't I email her, or use Facebook?'

I realise that he is probably afraid of rejection if this is his first attempt at asking a young lady out. It might be easier to face if it is done via a social network. There are also fewer people to know about his failure if this happened.

Oh Lord, asking can be such a difficult thing especially if I am really keen on getting the right answer. Getting what I want can get in the way of getting what I really need. Dear Father help me to accept the answer that you give me and the wisdom to know that it is what is best for me, as you know the whole picture, and I, only what I want.

So perhaps social networking would be a better way to ask a girl out; life seems to be more complicated now. I ask Henry if she is a friend of his on Facebook. He says not yet. I suggest that it might be a good way to see if she is interested in being his friend; at least it would be a start.

33

Little steps I think, especially for a novice. I tell him to go for it, as nothing ventured, nothing gained. He smiles and gives me a kiss on the forehead.

'Thanks mum,' he says and walks meaningfully away. Peace at last or at least till the next question.

Oh Lord, how grateful I am that my son will still ask me questions. I know that he might not accept my advice but having that connection is heartening, a little door still open.

Lily Pink is having problems with the computer; I can hear tones of frustration.

'Why can't you help me?' she says in a loud voice.

Sometimes I wonder if we ought to get the noise level tested in this house as it might well be over the designated level for normal living. It wouldn't surprise me if it was in the red or ready to explode section, like the fragile tempers in this abode. But Lily Pink is all or nothing and her determination will take her a long way, as well as be a contributing factor for a meltdown if she is not able to control it.

Oh Lord, how often have you seen those raging storms that afflict my life? High winds, whipping up anything in their way, pulling down fragile branches, exposing their weakness. When I pray to you, you calm my storm, heal what is broken and comfort my internal pain. Praise you God for understanding.

The crisis is over and Lily Pink is quiet again. I assume she has finished her homework, Johnny too, as the volume of the television in the sitting room, which is underneath me, makes me jump out of my skin. It is hastily turned down; someone must have hit the wrong button when they turned it on. Bob carries in two cups of tea. It is just what I need, hot and soothing. My head is still aching, but not too badly. Bob asks how my evening of relaxation has been! I laugh; it has been about as good as it gets with a household of six. I tell him that the only time I have ever been able to relax was when I was in hospital an hour or two after giving birth to the kids! Since then it has been manic but enormous fun.

Oh Lord, I can't Image how busy you are watching over us, for thousands of years. No wonder Heaven has no time, otherwise you would be exhausted. So next time I pray for a hurried decision on a matter, help me to wait for the right timing. For you a thousand years are but a day, and a day a thousand years. What a mystery. What a God.

It is not long before it is time to pack Lily Pink off to bed. But before Bob has finished his cup of tea the telephone rings. It is the gentleman we encountered in the hospital car park. The conversation isn't very long and Bob reassures the bereaved caller that his car will be safe in the hospital car park overnight, as long as it is locked. And yes it would be a good idea to call the RAC tomorrow for help. No it was no problem him calling, and Bob ended the conversation with a hope that things work out alright with the car, and a sorry about his mother's death.

Oh Lord, often all I need is a reassuring voice at the end of the phone when I am troubled. Thank you for all those times when I have rung a friend and they have been there for me. A listening ear, a gentle tone, an encouraging word. That is how I envision You when I talk to You.

All is relatively quiet now; Lily Pink has had a shower and gone happily to bed. Johnny got in and out of the shower showing it his body. Gabby plans to have one in the next half hour and Henry has decided that he will have his tomorrow morning. The sounds are peaceful, and I can only hear a clicking from a computer, probably Gabby, finishing her homework or maybe skype-ing. I would like to have a bath as I missed my shower this morning and find it more relaxing. But although my thoughts for it are willing, I feel exhausted. So I close my eyes and open my heart to prayer.

Oh Lord take my day's efforts and bless them. Thank you for your protection during the day for my husband, children and myself. May I have planted Your seed into the lives of others through my work and actions, so that when Your rain showers upon them they produce a rich harvest.

And in the silence that follows I hear a whisper from God:

Vicki, I love you.

Night Prayer

How good and how wonderful it is to be in the presence of God. Surrounded and in communion with the prayers of all the faithful.

Oh Lord, reveal to me the question that you asked of me today, the question that I have already said 'Yes' to.

And God replied:

My question was 'Will you allow me to be victorious in your life Victoria Sponge?'

What a question, what an ask. Will I allow God to be victorious in my life?

It's a bigger question than the priest asked me on the day of my wedding. Do I take this man, Bob Sponge, to be my lawful wedded husband? I was in love so the answer was easy. Am I in love with God enough to answer 'Yes', now I know the question.

And God interrupted my pondering and said:

Do you remember we threw away the recipe book when you became Victoria Sponge? That day of trust?

Yes I remembered, the same day I got married, I said Yes to a mature faith, a mature relationship. A faith that didn't rely on parent's beliefs, on a cradle religion, but on a relationship with God himself, up front and personal. A mature response taken and agreed by me for my salvation, to become the person God wants me to be for HIS honour and glory.

And that's the crux of it all. Why God died for me, because He wants me to be united with him in his victory. So I am ready for the question. Will I allow God to be victorious in my life?

I am Victoria Sponge. My ingredients have been weighed and measured, then blended together and cooked to perfection by God the

Father. I am light and delicate to the touch and adored by Jesus, injected with the finest filling, waiting to burst forth with the power of the Holy Spirit.

If you Father want me, a fool and a sinner, who has ruined his beautiful cake, then the answer is Yes. Definitely YES.

And God replied:

Then join me on this journey.

Chapter Two

Tuesday

Morning Prayer

'So do not fear, for I am with you; do not be dismayed, for I am your God. I will strengthen you and help you; I will uphold you with my righteous right hand.' - Almighty God; Isaiah 41:10 (New International Version)

Five past five in the morning. I have woken earlier than usual and can't get back to sleep. Morning Lord, I wonder what you have in store for me today. My answer this morning is 'Yes Father,' again to your question. I am excited as I know that today is a new beginning.

Oh Lord, for you there is no morning, afternoon, evening nor night time. No day, week, month or year. Everything just is, in your radiant glory. Because I don't understand your mysteries I question everything to try and comprehend; that is my adult mind. How is this or that possible? Well often it isn't, it just is. Like you. Why do I battle against this, why not just accept it? You are 'I AM'. You are Unconditional Love, no catch. No buy one ticket to heaven and get one free so long as you buy the right brand. You have already bought my ticket to Heaven by sending Jesus to save me. I am saved.

I am late; I must have drifted off again. The alarm forgot to go off; the alarm forgot to go off? It is plugged into the wall, it is on the mains. It can't not go off, unless there has been a power surge in the night. I shake Bob to wake him up, he grunts and turns over, he doesn't realise the urgency of the situation. I attempt to put on my dressing gown and have a fight with it instead. The arms are inside out, so I throw it on the floor and run downstairs into the garage, narrowly missing the pile of books lying on the floor. Whoever has a library in the garage? The switch is down, so I flick it up again, power is resumed.

Oh Lord, the day has just started and already I am in a panic. Give me your power to rouse the household into action and to stay calm.

I put the water on for a cup of tea and return to the bedroom. The early morning alarm is going off. Bob looks at the clock, he looks again, it finally registers that he is late, we are all late. He bursts from the bed, bangs on the girl's door, then on Henry's and Johnny's.

'Hurry up; it's nearly time for the bus!' Bob shouts.

Gabby appears, saying she needs to do her hair and have a shower first. She and Bob try to get into the bathroom at the same time. Gabby wins. Johnny is panicking as he hates being rushed. He is sporting a bandage around his left hand; it appears that Gabby has been practicing her first aid. Johnny seems happy with it so I decide to have a look at it after he gets home tonight from school. Henry just sprays himself and everything else with deodorant and decides he is ready. Meanwhile Lily Pink gets into our bed.

Oh Lord, why am I always so busy running? I feel like a hamster in its wheel, running but never really going anywhere. Please help me to find time in my day just to be and have some peace in your presence.

Everyone has departed the house so quickly that I feel unsettled. I feel the day has started without me. I don't know if the children took any lunch nor had any breakfast. Bob ran off with toast in his mouth mumbling something but I couldn't make out what he was saying. I assume Johnny made the bus with the others as no one has returned for a lift. Lily Pink appears to have gone and I don't remember her saying goodbye. Everything must have happened while I was in the shower. The house is like the Marie Celeste. Quiet and still. Apart from the cat that is cross because she hasn't been fed yet.

Oh Lord, my husband and children have gone to their daily institutions and I have no knowledge of what they are up to. I didn't even get my air kiss from Gabby. It might not be much but I missed it, missed her goodbye, missed everyone's goodbye. I wonder what they are all doing. Be with them all today Father, watch over them and bless all their efforts, for you see everything.

Immediately God speaks to me:
Come with me, I want to show you something. Draw closely into my Spirit.

Then God raises me high, higher than the clouds and opens up my world to one that is hidden in a teenagers mind. The vision becomes clear and I can see Gabby distinctly as if she were right next to me. I can hear her words and thoughts:

'I hate each morning travelling on the bus to school, it takes around half an hour but a lot can happen in that time. My friend isn't on it today, she says she has a cold, I expect she has testitis as we are being tested on the maths we have done so far this term'.

Texting:

'Are there tests in Heaven?'

Sending…..

Incoming text from G.O.L.D:

No, not if you know Me.

The bullying has started upstairs on the bus, Johnny is the recipient as usual and Henry defends his brother. I watch on wishing it to stop. Henry covers Johnny as a rotten banana is thrown his way. It catches Henry on the arm and splatters all over his uniform. Henry is beginning to see red. He gets up and heads toward the person who threw it, looms over him and aims a punch at the kid. But he doesn't follow through. He just glares and says, 'If I wanted to I could really hurt you, but you are not worth the effort.'

Texting:

'Why do people pick on my brother?'

Sending…..

Incoming text from G.O.L.D:

Because he is different. Remember I was different too.

'School looms up; I have no choice but to follow the crowd through its gates. I see one of my friends up ahead and start to walk faster. Lisa is my best friend. We talk about everything and anything. She looks excited about something, and when I catch up with her, she tells me that her father has managed to get two tickets for our favourite boy band. Oh joy of joys. My day has just got better.'

Texting:

'Thank you, thank you, thank you.'

Sending.…..

Incoming text from G.O.L.D:

I love to see you happy.

'The bell rings loud and clear, it is time to head for the morning lessons. After registration it is maths, at least the test will be done and out of the way. I look at the paper, it is easy, no problem. But I can see my friend Lisa is struggling.'

Texting:

'I don't get it, why do some people struggle and others find things easy?'

Sending.…..

Incoming text from G.O.L.D:

I give everyone talents; some are more obvious than others. Some are hidden waiting to be found, others are in the way they deal with their struggles.

'As we walk to our next lesson I put my arm around Lisa and tell her not to worry, she is brilliant at running and that is a handy talent to have as it gives stamina and strength to the mind and body. We chat about "Storming Warriors", our favourite boy band, and the concert

41

that we are going to go to in a couple of months. It is all we talk about during Physics behind our cupped hands. What was the homework? Oh doesn't matter I will message another friend later when I get home to get the details.'

Texting:

'Why do we need to do physics? What's so important about this subject?'

Sending…..

Incoming text from G.O.L.D:

You would not have IPods, computers, mobiles, radio, and hospital equipment without physics. You are a logical thinker, like to problem solve and are good at practical application; that's all physics too. Physics is cool. My Father loves physics.

'Wow that is cool. Well why didn't the teacher tell me this. So the Storming Warriors' equipment must be physics too. Now that is really something I can relate to. Maybe I will listen next time in lesson.'

Texting:

'Why do adults make everything complicated?'

Sending…..

Incoming text from G.O.L.D:

Because they have lost the eyes of a child and the wonderment of simplicity. They strive for knowledge to make them powerful, like Eve in the Garden of Eden when the snake said "If you eat from the tree of knowledge you will be like God, knowing everything." So in answer to your question adults are proud and don't like to look silly. The more they complicate things the more clever they think they are.

Texting:

'Are you saying that we shouldn't gain knowledge?'

Sending.....

Incoming text from G.O.L.D:

Knowledge is not a bad thing Gabby. Learning is important, school is important, but knowledge means that you have to be responsible with it. A good teacher knows this and helps his pupils to understand his subject in an exciting and enthusiastic way, wanting them to question it, to peel off its skin and discover its treasure. A bad teacher just says, "Hey look at me and all the knowledge I know," and don't share it in a way that a student can understand it.

'Lisa reminds me that we have assembly now. I wonder why assemblies are adult led. I sit there listening to someone who I find difficult to relate to. Sometimes they are talking down to us and other times it is over my head. I don't understand why they don't get that we would like to share our faith. Well some of us would, others would find it frightening thinking that they will be laughed at. But it would be nice to be asked.'

Texting:

'Why do adults think they know you better than us?'

Sending.....

Incoming text from G.O.L.D:

Love your question! Here's my suggestion, challenge them and see what happens.

Texting:

'How?'

Sending…..

Incoming text from G.O.L.D:

Ask for an audition. Allow them to see what you are capable of, how you can deliver your faith to your peers on an equal footing. Challenge them to let go of some of their assembly and put their trust in you. If you do this I will be with you, you will not be alone.

'I have just had an amazing thought. Why shouldn't we be part of an assembly? We could make it relevant, current, of interest to us. It would encourage us to speak out, be confident, and share our opinions. But would the adults allow it? It would mean they were not in control. Love that bit.'

I look at God as I can't quite believe what I am seeing and hearing. My daughter is communicating with her Father in Heaven. She normally gets upset with me if I mention anything about religion, but here she is texting God during her school day, and listening!

And God gazed gently upon me.

Why do you doubt your daughter's love of me? We text all the time using 'God On Line Direct'. It can be accessed instantly and is open 24/7.

All teenagers need is the right means of communication. Trust me with your daughter.

I am dumbfounded, but then I shouldn't be, we are a Christian family and we did agree to pass on our love of God to our children.

Oh Lord, I am so sorry for not trusting my daughter, for believing that she didn't care about you. For not trusting you, for asking you to change her heart, when it has already been claimed, for not believing in my faith.

Being a Christian mother is not easy Vicki that is why I wanted to encourage you.

44

The telephone rings in the distance. I am suddenly back at home feeling disorientated, so I let it ring a couple more times to get my head straight and then pick it up.

'This is a public service announcement, if you have taken out a loan in the last 10 years…..'

I hate those annoying calls, I tap the hash key frantically trying to disconnect, the voice goes on, 'press 5 now, if you have already……' Go away I yell, I never have had one, I don't want one, so stop calling me! Of course no one can hear me as it is pre-recorded, but it makes me feel better letting out my annoyance.

Oh Lord, how do these people get my phone number? I am ex-directory. Someone has breached my agreement. What would you do if that happened, if your agreement was breached? Oh Lord it was, by Judas, by money and a kiss and it led to the cross. In that case I can take a silly call once in a while, as the cross was the stepping stone to your resurrection to Your Victory.

Time is getting on and I need to get to the bank as there are various cheques that I have to put in. My mother and father-in-law tend to send a cheque to Lily Pink for her birthday, but instead of putting my name they put hers. I have told them lots of times that she doesn't have a bank account, but each year the cheques come and I have the same rigmarole at the bank as they won't take the cheques with someone else's name on other than mine. I have two with my name on and two with another name. I write the counter slip and put one of mine on top and the other on the bottom.

Oh Lord, I am sorry if I am being deceitful, but it is only a little indiscretion and the money will go to Lily Pink anyway.

At the bank there is a long queue as usual. Old people mainly. The first counter has a gentleman who seems to have raided his piggy bank, as pennies crash all over the place while he pushes the coins through the glass opening. The assistant looks harassed as she tries to count all the small change. The gentleman keeps interrupting saying that there is ten pounds, and she doesn't need to count it as he already has. The second counter is closed; behind it there is a lady sitting doing something on

45

the computer and looks up every so often and then returns to what she is doing. The third counter is empty, and the forth counter is for enquires only. So we are all waiting for the first counter. The tension is beginning to build in me, do I look guilty, do I look like I am trying to be deceptive, and will the assistant accept my cheques without looking at them too closely? The wait is making me nervous.

Oh Lord, why do I do this to myself? I know that I am no good at pulling the wool over people's eyes, they always see through me. This isn't a major attempt at fraud, so why do I feel so guilty? Please help me to do my banking and get out of here quickly. Or is that asking you to be an accomplice? In that case I accept the outcome rather than drag you through my mess.

At last it is my turn. I look at the lady and she smiles at me, she asks what she can do for me today. I pass my paying in book through and she takes out each cheque, carefully in silence, and as if in slow motion, checks each then looks at me. I am informed that only two can be banked. I sigh, and ask about the other two. The assistant says that I must open an account for my daughter in order to bank the cheques. I nod my head and question if this can be done now. She says no, not without my daughter and in any case no one is there to do the paper work. A bank refusing money because they haven't got the staff! I find this quite funny but also annoying. I suggest that it would be easier if she just banked the cheques and ignored the names on them, but the assistant stated that head office would be very unhappy if she did that. But wouldn't head office be upset if they knew that money was being refused because of a lack of common sense? She said that I could be putting in anyone's cheque. I just looked at her. They have the same surname on them I mention. But the lady remained adamant, rules were rules.

Oh Lord, well I did say that I would accept the verdict. But I have to admit that I am frustrated with it all. I suppose the assistant was right. She obeyed the rules, crossed the t's and dotted the i's for her Head Office. Help me to accept that this lady was only doing her job and there was no ill will in her actions.

Having left the bank I walk along the street to the main centre of the town. On the way I meet an acquaintance whose son used to be friends with Johnny. She smiles and says hallo. We exchange pleasantries.

46

'How's what's his name, your son, with the problems?' I glare at her, never having discussed my son or his issues with her.

'Johnny is doing very well thank you,' I respond. Then she realises that her comment wasn't a very nice one, apologises for her tactlessness, and goes into a high speed speech about her amazing son and all he is achieving at the moment.

Oh Lord, I am about to commit a sin if I don't get away from this lady….

I bite my lip and try to edge away, looking at my watch and stating that it is time to fly. She is still in mid flow when I leave her. How dare this lady refer to my son as the one with the problems? How rude of her. Where did she get that opinion from? He has a name, Johnny, and he is special, like all my children are. I don't see him as a problem, he finds life challenging but then don't we all.

Oh Lord, aaaaah, have you anything more frustrating for me this morning? There is still time. Father I feel angry at that lady's comment. Help me to forgive her and not let her words eat away at me during the rest of the day.

I return to the car park where I left my car and realise that I don't remember where it is. I rub my head hoping for inspiration, but only feel the bump from yesterday and wince as it is painful to touch. My remote door lock doesn't work as the battery died earlier in the year, so I can't use it to detect my car. The car park isn't that big, but for some reason everyone with a blue Corsa has parked there today. At last I find it, put the key in the lock but nothing happens, it remains shut. I try again and again. Nothing. Then an irate gentleman comes storming up to me accusing me of trying to steal his car. I try to calm the man by reassuring him that this was in fact my car. He pushes me out of the way and puts his key into the lock, it opens. I apologise profusely, I can't understand how I made such a mistake. A policeman who is returning to his squad car with a sausage roll and coffee comes over. I panic, do I run or do I stay. Then I realise that I haven't actually done anything wrong apart from mistake this man's car for my own, so I stay.

Oh Lord, mistakes happen, same car, colour, make and it is also in need of a clean.

There is one number difference on the licence plate, a small difference, but the one decisive factor that makes it unique. So I got it wrong, thank God I am human.

The police officer is asking if the gentleman wants to press charges. He sighs and realises that I am in fact in a bit of a state, with a nasty bruise on my forehead which might account for my actions. He shakes his head with a negative and suggests that the policeman try and help me find my own car. It doesn't take long and is only a few cars away.

'Life Sucks, 52, Don't Give Up,' I say out loud.

The policeman looks at me, 'I beg your pardon?'

I repeat the letters and numbers, LS52 DGU; I tell him that it is my number plate. He asks me if I am okay and I just raise my shoulders and comment that it has been one of those mornings and I shall be alright once I have had a cup of coffee. He leaves me there and we both drive out of the car park, him following me for a short way and then turning off down a side road.

Oh Lord, I must appear quite strange to some people. Maybe a better word for me is unique, because I am one of a kind. Thank you Father that when I was born you broke the mould.

And when I pull into my driveway and stop the car, God utters:

Vicki, you are perfect in my eyes. You are right; there can be no one else like you, not now or ever. Your being was thought of even before time began.

Afternoon Prayer

As I am eating my lunch the telephone rings. I am half inclined to leave it but then something prompts me to answer it. My friend Cathy is on the other end, crying and talking in an indecipherable manner. I tell her that I am on my way round to her place and will be with her in a minute. Fortunately Cathy lives in the next road.

Oh Lord, help me to know how to help my friend. Please give me the words to say that will comfort and uplift her.

When Cathy opens her front door her face is red and blotchy, she has obviously been crying for a while. I give her a long hug and then she invites me in. We go and sit in her front room. It is tidy and comfortable. Then I wait for my friend to tell me what is wrong. It takes a while of silence and hand holding before Cathy is able to tell me what is troubling her.

Oh Lord, I really need your wisdom to help me now.

I have never seen her as upset as this before. My lovely friend is crumbling before my eyes. She looks at me and slowly takes a deep breath. She tells me about her husband James, he is upstairs sleeping having been given some tablets to help calm him down, as he has been under a lot of stress recently. Then the story unfolds of Cathy's husband being told that his job was on the line. All managers were being asked to reapply for their jobs which also involved taking on a very large work load, that of two other members of staff who would then be made redundant.

Oh Lord, how can this be fair? One man coping with a work load of three, it sounds like madness. Thank you Father that you have only given us the cross that we can carry. Not too heavy, too long nor too wide, just right for our backs.

James hadn't agreed with the way things were being done and he made an official complaint. He was told that because he had mental health problems and the new job role would be unsuitable for his stress levels it would be better if he took redundancy. James had been surprised that his period of sickness for mental exhaustion five years ago was being

49

brought up now. He hadn't had a day off sick since, as he had changed his lifestyle to a healthier one. He had asked his colleagues to back him up as the new regime would be unworkable. They had turned their back on him as they were afraid of losing their jobs too. It would be dog eat dog for the few positions that would be available. James took the redundancy reluctantly with a bitter heart and the pressure from the whole incident had knocked him for six. He was now behaving very erratically. He had hit Cathy in the stomach in an angry fit last night and she had called the doctor out as she was frightened about what he might do next.

Oh Lord, you know what it is to be deserted and left with your anguish, knowing that the days ahead would be at times unbearable. Help me to know how to support my friend in her time of trial and tribulation. Don't let me fall asleep to her needs.

Cathy looks exhausted and frightened. She has finished her dialogue and the two words that come to my mind are protection and companionship. We sit quietly and then I suggest that we pray there and then for her and James. After a few minutes we hear a noise from upstairs, it sounds like James is up and moving around. Cathy looks at me and asks me not to go yet. It is two thirty and I have another half an hour before I have to be back for Lily Pink.

Oh Lord, let not my time constraints affect this situation.

James enters the room and says that he is hungry. He doesn't seem to register that I am there. Cathy and I go to the kitchen and she prepares a cup of tea and a sandwich for her husband. When we go back into the sitting room James is sitting staring into space, with a blank look on his face. Cathy hands him the cup of tea and sandwich. James suddenly takes and throws the plate with the sandwich across the room and then knocks the cup of tea out of Cathy's hand. The result is mayhem, Cathy is jumping round with hot tea all over her, James is screaming that he doesn't want anything and uses volatile language. He is beside himself with rage, calling Cathy all sorts of horrid names. This is so unlike James. I rush Cathy to the bathroom and tell her to spray herself with the cold water from the shower. Then I run downstairs and see that James is on the floor crying and slamming his fists on the carpet uncontrollably, unable to stop the flood of despair overtaking him. I do

50

the only thing I can and phone for an ambulance.

Oh Lord, when darkness takes over a life and mayhem is all around seeking to consume it, send your angels to fight and conquer the battle. I am scared Father, this situation is out of my control. Please bring help quickly.

The crew of the ambulance are amazing, one goes upstairs to see Cathy and help her with the scalding effects of the tea and the other takes charge of James. The professional is wonderful and soothes and calms James enough to get him into the ambulance. The crew having heard about the incident don't think that it is a good idea that Cathy goes in the same vehicle as James, so I volunteer to take her to hospital to get her injuries checked out. I am aware that Lily Pink will be coming home soon and that I won't be around to let her in. I quickly knock on another neighbour's door and ask them if they will take Lily Pink in until I get back from the hospital. Fortunately they agree.

Oh Lord, thank you for sending me your angels in the form of ambulance employees and neighbours. Bless their willingness to help and make a difficult situation more manageable.

The hospital decides to admit James and treat Cathy for her burns. Because we were so quick in applying cold water, Cathy has been lucky; her face won't be too scarred. However the shock will take longer to get over. Before we leave the hospital, we have to go to the ward where James is. The staff asks Cathy to stay for a while in order to get the background information on what has been happening to James. Then we are told that her husband is comfortable and that Cathy must go home and get some rest as she has been through a traumatic experience. She is to call the next day as it will take time to assess James and decide on the best treatment plan for him. They say it is possible that he will be transferred to the local specialist hospital depending on the psychiatric report.

Oh Lord, give my friend courage; it must be so painful to see her beloved husband in such anguish. Please heal her own scars so that her face and mind are not disfigured in any way. Thank you Father, that I was there and available in her time of need.

I drive us back home and ask Cathy if she would like to stay with me and have a cup of tea at my house. She is reluctant but then decides that it might be helpful. I quickly run over to the neighbour who has Lily Pink and collect her. Lily Pink notices Cathy's face and asks if she is alright. L P tells my friend that she wants to be a nurse one day. I unlock the door and we go in. I look for any hazards on the floor, not wanting anyone to take a fall. All is clear for once. I suggest that Cathy sit in the front room where it is comfortable and quiet. Or at least it is until Lily Pink puts on the television. So Cathy moves to the dining room, which seems like a better idea.

Oh Lord, I know that a cup of tea isn't going to make everything alright, but companionship and love is all I can give at the moment. Please may that be enough to help my friend.

It seems difficult to ask my friend how she is feeling now, as no doubt she will be feeling awful. So I just put my hand on her shoulder and place a cup of tea in front of her, understanding if she decides that she would rather not have it considering what happened with the last cup she had contact with. Just in case I place a glass of water next to it so that she has the choice. Cathy looks at me and asks if James will be alright. I am hesitant, not sure what to say. 'With help and time he will,' I figure.

Oh Lord, all things are possible with you. You know my comings and goings, physically, mentally and spiritually. These are subject to good health as well as illness. You can cure anything if it is your will for us. Grant me acceptance of Your will when times are good as well as troubled.

I inform Cathy that the house is about to become alive with hungry and irrational behaviour. I emphasise that I want her to stay, but she doesn't feel that she can handle the banter of teenagers. I fully understand; I'm not sure I can either. We hug and I tell her that I will pop in later to see how she is. Cathy mouths a thank you, opens the front door and without being asked Lily Pink takes her hand and walks my friend back home slowly.

Oh Lord, thank you for the understanding of youth, their sensitivity at times of need. I am so grateful that my daughter has this gift. May she never lose it.

The key to a happy teenager (other than removing their hormones or having a teenage brain translator) is a full stomach, but that often doesn't happen as they are always hungry. You can feed them and feed them and they still want more. Usually I try to have a meal nearly ready for when the hungry monsters arrive so that I can give it to them as soon as possible. Otherwise they raid the cupboards for anything and will eat without discretion. Today I am not ready, so I take whatever I can find that they might eat, and quickly put it in the garage, on top of the book shelves. I hastily put on some mince for spaghetti bolognaise, only to remember that Gabby hates mince. Tough, I think. I know that she won't go hungry, and it is her choice if she refuses her meal and I haven't got time for a fussy eater.

Oh Lord, feed me. Give me food for life, water me, refresh my enthusiasm for you. Help me not to feed only on those things that bring me instant satisfaction, but instead encourage me to replenish from your everlasting food source.

Henry, Johnny and Gabby arrive home all together with Lily Pink in tow.

'What's for tea?' they all chorus.

When I respond, there are two urrhs and two yummies. Well 50% isn't bad. With that, all disappear immediately upstairs and the noise begins. I can roughly pick out music from One Dimension, which is tolerable, Storming Warriors latest number one, with lyrics that appear undecipherable and Hope's rendition of 'I want to be free'. Don't we all! I assume Lily Pink is listening to Storming Warriors with Gabby as there appears no protesting at the moment over choice of music from that quarter.

Oh Lord, how wonderful it must be to hear everything as music to your ears. No confliction of genre; all harmonious and beautiful, creating a thrill to the senses. Please help my family to move towards that heavenly scene.

The spag bol takes twenty minutes, and is bubbling gently away, time enough to get some washing on. In the bathroom the wash bin is almost empty; that can only mean one thing, dirty washing in the bedrooms, no doubt all over the floor. I knock on Henry's door and ask for his whites. The door opens a fraction and I am handed a couple of pairs of pants.

'Is that all?' I ask.

Henry does a quick look round and says 'yes'. I have obviously caught him at an inopportune moment as he seems eager to close the door.

'Any shirts?'

He knows I know that there are, and he pushes the door to and I can hear rummaging and things being moved around. He opens the door a fraction and hands me some more clothing while looking at something of greater interest.

'Socks?' I enquire, then I remember he doesn't wear white socks as they are not cool.

Oh Lord, however hard I try to hide my secrets, I am usually found out. That faltering answer, look of guilt, fidgeting, no matter if it is a good secret, like a surprise, or the opposite, a lie, both get detected. With You Father nothing is a secret, because everything you do is for my good.

Next I venture to the girls room, I knock out of respect, but the music is too loud. So I bang loudly. Another face at the door.

'Yes?' Gabby questions.

'Dirty whites?'

She looks at me and raises her eyes.

'Now?'

I tell her that it would be helpful as I want to get a load on. The door is closed on me again; I can feel a pattern here! From inside the music is stopped as the raised voices are having problems competing with the noise.

'She wants what?' Lily Pink yells and then realises that she doesn't need to.

'What now?'

More shuffling and scurrying from the occupants to find their dirty laundry. The door opens and a pile is pushed into my arms hurriedly and the door closes. Thank you I say to a poster of a dark haired boy staring at me!

Oh Lord, I seem to be competing with a cacophony of sounds. It is exhausting making me heard in this environment. Please Father keep me in tune with what is important.

Johnny's door is slightly ajar, not by much but enough for me to peer in with one eye. He is lying on his bed with his face towards the wall, legs pulled up to his chest and his arms cradling them. His music isn't as loud as the others, but it is rather melancholy. I tap loud enough to be heard. Johnny looks towards me. I can see that he is not happy. I sigh as I hate to see him forlorn. I throw the washing into a heap on the bathroom floor, and then request permission to enter his room. He shrugs, meaning 'whatever'. The kitchen is underneath Johnny's room and I can hear a faint ringing sound. The tea is ready. Great timing I think. Its one of those dilemmas, teenager needs a little attention, food needs dealing with or it gets ruined, hungry people waiting for meal.

Oh Lord, a three way challenge. Listen, act or delegate. What would you do all three at once maybe? You are the God of the impossible.

I say to Johnny that I will be back in two shakes. He just turns his head and resumes staring at the wall. Meanwhile I gather the troops and tell them that tea is waiting for them to dish up and that I would like a tray of food for Johnny in his room. They head downstairs at a pace, plates rattle. I image the spag bol being slopped onto them with gusto. Henry appears with Johnny's. I mouth, 'anything I should know?' and he says 'bad day at school'. I wonder if it is to do with his hand, I had forgotten to write him a letter of excuse asking some sympathy for Johnny's injury.

55

Oh Lord, isn't it amazing how quickly my brood can muster themselves when food is mentioned. But food isn't on Johnny's mind Father. With Your help guide me in how to release him from whatever is binding Johnny and making him so unhappy.

The doorbell rings and rings and rings. Everyone is too busy eating to do anything about it. Then there is a banging of frustration on the door and a call for help.

'Will someone please open this thing?' yells Bob through the letter box.

I apologise to Johnny once again and make my way down to the front door. Bob has his hands full of books, I ask how he managed to press the door bell, and he looks upwards, with his head it appears. I don't ask if he used his head to bang on the door as well! He wobbles in not knowing if there are any traps ahead of him. I tell him that tea is on the stove and that I need to give Johnny some one to one time. He grunts and moves cautiously towards the kitchen on route to the garage.

Oh Lord, it is so easy to get side-tracked with treasures of this world. Help me to keep my eyes on the real treasure trail that leads to your kingdom.

As I take the first steps towards my son's perplexing situation, God offers me some advice.

Remember Johnny loves you.

Evening Prayer

I have struggled with Johnny ever since he was born. His twin sister Gabby would laugh at things whereas he just looked. She crawled, he bottom shuffled. She spoke non-stop, he stayed silent. I thought he was just letting Gabby take the lead. But something told me things were not quite right in his little world. He looked worried all the time about everything. His life wasn't as carefree as Gabby's.

Oh Lord, my world has been created by who I am, and at times it is very confusing and seems upside down in comparison to others. Please help me not to look at others to see if my world is on a par with theirs. The world I live in is precisely that, 'my world' neither right nor wrong, just fashioned to fit my life and where I am in it today.

As I knock and enter Johnny's room again, he is still in the same position. His tray of food has not been touched. I sit on the bottom of his bed and just wait. You can't rush Johnny especially when he needs to share something, but isn't sure how to. He points to his blazer and says 'top pocket'. There is a piece of paper sticking up out of it, folded into four. I open it and read the contents. It is brief and to the point. It states that my son is thick, but in a crass way. I fold it up and put it in my pocket. Then he points to his rucksack, I look inside and see a horrible mess. There is rice pudding all over his books. I close my eyes and wonder what type of person would do this to my son.

Oh Lord, no wonder my son is upset. In fact he must be furious and ready to explode. But he is just lying here on the bed, staring into nothingness. My heart bleeds for him Father. How does he cope with this? How do I cope with this in a way that will help him?

I want to hug Johnny, but he is not a hugger. I want to tell him that everything will be sorted and these boys will not do this again. But I know he doesn't believe that. I want to scream out with rage at the unfairness of it all. Where were his friends when this was happening? Did no one stand up for him at school? Have the teachers seen this? Where were they when it happened? I want some answers, but Johnny just stares at the wall.

Oh Lord, how cruel some people are. I want justice, I am angry, frustrated that my son is being bullied. What right have they to make my son's life miserable? Father, deliver my son from his persecutors.

I look at Johnny and say out loud that we need to deal with this.

He suddenly sits upright and bursts into tears, sobbing out the words, 'no, it will just get worse.'

But I know that the bullies can't be allowed to get away with this sort of prank. There has to be a way of putting an end to it.

Oh Lord, you encountered many bullies in your life. You understand what he is going through. Help me to find a way to disarm them with your knowledge.

I try to reason with Johnny, but he is not listening. He can't cope with this amount of pain. He takes a deep breath in between his sobs and then a gush of abuse comes rushing out. He says he hates me, **(remember Johnny loves you)** hates himself, hates his life, and hates God. He wants it all to end, he has had enough and he knows how to kill himself. It would be best for all of us if he were not alive. He is too much trouble, a nuisance to us all and he would be better off dead. I am stunned, shocked by his intensity. Tears form in my eyes.

Oh Lord, my beautiful boy, my special boy, my courageous boy who fought for his life as a baby, brought so low in this moment by the deeds of insensitive and thoughtless school boys. I cry to you my Father in Heaven; carry this burden that is so heavy on my son's heart. Cradle him in your arms and give him hope.

I am desperate to hug my son. I plead with him to allow me to cuddle him, but he just curls up into a ball, rolls onto his side and pulls the duvet over himself. It is all too much, even a mother's love in the form of a hug. Johnny is exhausted; the exertion of speaking his thoughts in such a forceful way has driven him to a fitful sleep. I feel that I can't leave him in this state of mind, but I know that he needs to rest.

Oh Lord, as my son sleeps, speak to him. Let him feel and know your love for him. Father, heal the hurt, deliver him from the effects of this assault made upon his spirit. And protect his raging mind from thoughts of self-harm.

As Johnny sleeps I pray for him, knowing that my prayers are enfolding him and are as close to his heart as my hugs would be. Having prayed protection over my son's life, I take his tray of food with the knife and fork out of his room, put it on the hall floor and then go back for the ruck sack. When leaving my son's room I partly close the door. I want to know when he is awake again.

Oh Lord, help me; I can't cope with this without you by my side.

I find Bob in the kitchen with Henry, Gabby and Lily Pink. They can see that I am upset. I put the tray down and then open Johnny's bag. They all try to peep inside. Henry is the first to react; he loves Johnny dearly and feels that he is his responsibility at school. He tenses up furious at the insulting evidence. He wants revenge.

Oh Lord, it is hard to turn the other cheek when things are personal, when the weak are targeted by the pack. But this is a universal reality that happens all over the world. Where are you in all of this?

I am not in the sin; I am in the victory Vicki.

Henry walks off with his head down; he feels he has failed his brother. His only solution at this moment is to go outside and kick hell out of anything he can find to hit against. Meanwhile Gabby's face is telling its own story. It is red and blotchy with fury in her eyes, but she doesn't let it erupt over. Gabby puts on an apron and then gets some newspaper and lays it on the floor. She takes the bag and slowly and gently picks out the contents and lays them on the sheets of paper. The slimy excretion is everywhere. Lily Pink wants to know why there is rice pudding in her brother's bag.

Oh Lord, there is always good among the mess. I have a choice here, be overcome by the enormity of the situation, get bogged down with the idea of retribution or accept what has happened and help with the clean-up operation. Father, help me not let the sin control my actions.

Bob and I take each item and clean them as best as we can. The stains will leave evidence of this day. Bob remains quiet through the whole procedure, but I know that he is hurting inside, his family has been attacked, and as protector this is painful for him. The bag looks ruined as it is material and will in time smell because of the milky content stuck to it. It is Johnny's favourite and one that even though it has seen better days he will not part with. He loves its smell, just like the awful comforters he would hang onto when he was a baby. No amount of coaxing would prize the beloved item from him to be washed. But now I have no choice, it is washing or binning and hopefully it will survive the machine.

Oh Lord, I need to be cleansed and renewed so that my spirit does not become sour and spoiled. Father, wash me in your fragrance and light.

The books we place on the dining room table to dry out, fortunately they all have been laminated to preserve them from the rigours of everyday school life. Lily Pink still wants to know how the rice pudding got into the bag. The dessert has managed to find its way into everything and the pages inside the books are tainted with its smear as well. There isn't much we can do about this so we spray them with Fabreze and hope for the best. Bob looks fit to burst; he excuses himself and says he is going to check on Johnny. I haven't told him yet about his son's desperate plea to end it all.

Oh Lord, just oh Lord.

Henry re-enters the kitchen from the garden. I hug him, he is as tall as me and I can feel his heart pounding through his t-shirt. I reassure him that we will get this matter sorted. He grunts not believing that this is possible. I think he has his own agenda. He says he wants to see Johnny; he wants to know who did it. I tell him that his father is with his brother at the moment and he needs to give them time together.

Oh Lord, it is a natural response to want to retaliate, but it is not always the best or right answer. Two wrongs don't make a right, even if it does make us feel better having done something about a situation. I want to do something about this situation, but I want to do the right thing, the right thing that will help Johnny not make it worse. Father I place this into your hands as mine are not trustworthy at the moment.

The telephone rings, it is Cathy; she is desperate to talk and for company. I am torn; my time is full with this crisis. I don't want to desert her in her time of need. I gently tell her that I really want to help her but we have a difficult situation at the moment and I need to be at home to help my family. I suggest that she rings Paula, our friend from church, who is part of our support circle and reassured Cathy that I will ring her later when I can. I put the phone down; sometimes life just isn't easy, there is no simple solution.

Oh Lord, I feel exhausted, emotionally flat, physically drained and the day hasn't finished yet.

Bob returns, he says that Johnny is still sleeping. We go into the dining room and sit at the table, looking at the results of our clean-up effort. Gabby has gone upstairs with Lily Pink to wash themselves. I take this opportunity to tell Bob that his son is at crisis point, that he has had enough, wants out of this life. Bob puts his head in his hands and sobs. I put my arms around him and pray.

Oh Lord, I have no words, you know my prayer, my plea, and you see our distress. Come.

I know that we need to come together as a family and talk about what has happened as it affects us all. When Bob has exhausted his tears I go and round up the other three. We go into the sitting room where we can sit comfortably alongside one another. The faces all look towards me, they want answers and so do I. I ask what is going on at school with Johnny and why we have not been told about the bullying.

Henry and Gabby look at each other. 'We didn't want to bother you'.

I tell them that it has gone way past the 'not bothering us' point. They agree and apologise but defend themselves saying that nothing is done about bullying at school. I remind them that not knowing isn't the same as ignoring it. Were the school aware of the situation? Had one of them talked to a teacher, on Johnny's behalf? They shake their heads. So how can the school to do anything if they haven't been told? The point is taken. Next step, a united family prayer time and reassurances that tomorrow Bob and I will deal with the situation with the help of the school.

61

Oh Lord, the mistake was to try and cope with the situation in our own strength. I hand over to you my mistakes, my need to sort things out, my short sightedness which complicates the solution. Help me to be a part of your victory in this situation.

I know that the praying and unity in this sadness has helped us all. Johnny needs our unification and family strength to help him get through this. Lily Pink still finds it hard to understand why anyone would be so unkind to her brother. She decides to write him a letter of love and when she finishes it she quietly takes it to his room and places it on his pillow for him to read when he awakes. I enter Johnny's room after Lily Pink as I want to check his hand. Underneath the bandage I see a red mark which is not as bad as I was envisioning. The water certainly helped and now it needs the healing qualities of the air. As I leave my son I am surprised at the lateness of the hour and encourage all to get ready for bed. Then I ring Cathy and she is a bit calmer having spent time with Paula. I feel relieved about that.

Oh Lord, finish what we have started in our prayers and give us all the rest we need.

And God responds:

Vicki, you will always find your rest in me.

Night Prayer

The day is nearly done and the night is closing in fast. Today has been a challenge. I take a deep breath. The rucksack has been washed and dried; it is fresh, but feels and looks different. The logo has gone along with a lot of the grime. I hope it will be acceptable in Johnny's sight. And now I turn to the matters of my soul.

Oh Lord, reveal to me your question that I answered so long ago this morning. What did I say 'yes' to today and did I succeed in my answer to your question?

Vicki, I asked you to be with me in the garden of Gethsemane, to stay awake and be of comfort to me in my time of anguish, and you were. You were not found asleep or failing in your response. Thank you for joining me in my victory today for being open to my call.

When was I at Gethsemane Lord?

When you comforted and supported Cathy. I was there in need of help. When you listened to your son's anguish I was weeping too. And when your heart was breaking at the sight of your son's agony, my sweat fell to the ground like great drops of blood.

(See Luke 22 v 44)

I reflect on these words and thank God for his company during my day. I ask for the Spirit to comfort all my family during the night. I know that this cup is not going to be taken away and that I must accept the Father's will in my life and in the lives of my family. And I pray fervently for strength and the company of angels to fight our battle against the injustice of my son's situation. I pray too for Bob and Henry who are angry and want to pursue their own sense of justice. I feel I have done all I can now. The night is closing in and I need to sleep, my body and mind are aching from the mixture of feelings that have been in the ingredients of the day.

Oh Lord, saviour and baker, restore this Sponge, its flagging middle to rise again to its full glory through the power of your energy and perfect temperature. Sieve the fine sprinkles of the Spirit over me and allow the beautiful aroma of a freshly baked Sponge to bring new hope to those around me.

Dear Vicki, thank you for your prayer and submission to my will. No matter what ingredients I have made you with, I only ever use the best, as I only make perfect cakes and I love Victoria Sponge.

Chapter Three

Wednesday

Morning Prayer

'Blessed is the one who perseveres under trial because, having stood the test, that person will receive the crown of life that the Lord has promised to those who love him.' - James, disciple of Jesus; James 1:12 (New International Version)

I can see a beautiful sunrise outside my window, what a glorious start to this day. How awesome this God made creation is. From where else could such a spectacular image have been thought of apart from the Heavenly Kingdom? How small and insignificant we are in comparison to the palate of colours of an artist's mind. And yet we are important to the Creator, so significant that we are central to his plan, and his infectious love that denies no one access to His Wedding. But are we ready, am I ready? Is my Yes ready for another day? A day when I know we have to allow God's say to be paramount, and not necessarily to answer our wants but to give us our needs.

Oh Lord, who is in Heaven, I worship your name. Your glory be in our lives, Your kingdom come, here and now in my yes to the Father. Give me today, your merciful strength, as I seek to forgive those that have hurt my family and help me not to hold onto the sin that will damage my soul.

I look at Bob's side of the bed; it hasn't been slept in all night. As it is only six o'clock I tiptoe to each room and check on everyone. Henry, Gabby and Lily Pink are all fast asleep. In Johnny's room I find Bob side by side with our son. He looks exhausted and not someone who has had a refreshing sleep. Bob slowly and carefully pulls himself up from the bed and slips out from under the duvet. Bob used to snuggle in with Johnny when he was little and the night time monsters scared him. Now it wasn't night time monsters, but daytime terrors instead.

Oh Lord, night time can bring many terrors that unnerve me. My imagination runs riot and even the most innocuous shapes or noises arouse my senses when I am delicate and insecure. You Father have the power to release me from my fears,

65

empower me now for this day.

I ring up my preschool manager and friend early so that she can organise cover for me and explain briefly why I am unable to come in this morning. She prays with me there and then that God's Will will be triumphant during the course of the day. Bob also has decided to take the day off work. He will call in as soon as he knows that the manager is there and explain why he needs time off. His manager, fortunately, is approachable, and Bob doesn't think that there will be a problem. We agree to let Johnny stay at home for the day if he wants to, but will have to take him into school with us to give a description of the perpetrators. I know that Johnny will find it difficult to finger his fellow students. Hiding seems far more attractive, less noticeable, and that is how he has tried to survive till now no doubt. But he has been found and betrayed.

Oh Lord, I believe in you, in Your Spirit of Truth. May it reign through today.

There is a sombre mood in the house as everyone wakes up and gets ready for school. No one seems to want to talk, just to get on with their necessary tasks before leaving. Henry and Gabby ask if Johnny is going to school as time is getting on, and accept that it might be better if he stays away today. Each hugs me on their way out, a sign of unison in our joint concern for a family member. Lily Pink finds the atmosphere strange but knows that it is best to share the experience and once the front door is closed runs off to find her friends and to catch the bus.

Oh Lord, we know that today is going to be difficult. There will be denials and friendships tested, brick walls and collusion. You have already been through all of this before. Please carry us through the sea of lies into the rays of righteousness.

Bob has just called his manager and all is okay for him to have the day off. He then contacts the school and asks for an urgent appointment with the Head of Year. We are fortunate as he is able to see us at ten thirty this morning.

Oh Lord, thank you for arranging this.

We both go in to see Johnny. He is awake but sullen. I ask if he would like some breakfast but he refuses it. I tell him that we have an

66

appointment with his Head of Year and he just looks at me and stays silent. I suggest that he gets up and has a shower before we leave for the meeting. He turns over, with his back to me, suggesting that the conversation is now over. I look at Bob and we retreat from the room.

Oh Lord, thank you that you did not retreat from your calling, that you found the Higher strength to fulfil your destiny. I praise and worship you.

Bob puts on the kettle and we sit in the dining room quietly. I wonder what thoughts are going through his intelligent mind. How does he comprehend this act of insane cruelty? What could justify this bizarre behaviour by other teenagers? What pleasure would they get from this taunting? But Bob says nothing.

Oh Lord, from the beginning of time we have been following our own way, doing cruel and insane deeds to our fellow man. What drives us to do such things? We are capable of doing gross acts of cruelty, but also mighty acts of kindness. And yet you still stick up for us, you still died for us. Thank God you are in charge.

I hear footsteps on the floor boards upstairs above us. Johnny is up. The water system starts up so he must be preparing to have a shower. I feel that that is a good thing. I don't want to have to persuade Johnny to come with us; I want it to be his choice, his decision to take action against his bullies.

Oh Lord, I know that I ought not to fight my children's battles for them, it has to be a conscious decision by them to right the wrongs, asking for help and advice when it is needed. However, it is very difficult to just watch and I know that I am not a watcher. I like action, doing something to make things better. Perhaps this makes things worse in their world for them. If so, then I am guilty and am sorry for interfering with their attempts to sort out their own problems. Standing back is so difficult Lord, especially with Johnny who seems to attract more unwanted attention than most from stronger peers. Please guide me, so that what I do does not create more injury and provoke a harsher response from those that seek to undermine and discredit my son.

Johnny joins us at the dining room table; he sits down in a resigned manner. He asks what time we have to go. I look at my watch and tell him that we have about an hour before making the trip to his school.

Johnny gets up and goes into the sitting room and turns the television on. He wants to be distracted no doubt. I decide to ring Cathy to see how her night has been and to hear of any news concerning James.

Oh Lord, sometimes I need a distraction, especially if my mind is occupied with a troubled problem and I am not able to see a solution. I know that when you needed time away, You took yourself off to a quiet spot to be alone with your Father. In the market place of life help me to find that inner quiet.

There is no answer from Cathy's telephone, so I assume that she is either occupied and can't hear the ring, out of the house, or just doesn't want to answer at this early hour. Whichever it is I offer up a prayer for her and leave things in His hands. Bob has remembered about the cup of tea and brings in a lukewarm dark brown liquid. I accept it for what it is and drink it down straight away. Bob just leaves his on the table and turns on the computer to see what the news is, another distraction technique. The main heading on the internet page is about the Government wanting to claw back money from the poor, unemployed and generally disaffected members of society, so what's new. Bob says out loud something about 'the lot of them being crooks, dishonest and perpetually hoodwinking the population'; I think he means the Government.

Oh Lord and gardener, nothing has changed, those in power exploiting the weak. You have seen it ever since mankind stepped out of the Garden of Eden. I have these traits and know that you take time to prune me so that they do not creep up the walls of my life and become embedded in my response to the needs of others.

Bob fingers a headline.

'I don't believe it' he says 'there's a picture of my old headmaster.'

Sure enough Paul Fraxton is staring at us. I look to see why, and just as I am about to read the first line, the computer crashes. Typical! I look at Bob for the answer and he just shrugs his shoulders and says he doesn't know. I think the face from the past was a bit of a shock for him, they never really got on and Bob very rarely talks about his time at school. So I am left wondering. The internet continues to register 'no connection', and I remain none the wiser.

Oh Lord, faces from the past, or incidents that trigger pains from the past are always difficult to think about. Father help me when my triggers are pulled and leave me vulnerable.

I roll my tongue over my teeth and realise that I haven't cleaned them yet; in fact I am not sure if I have cleaned anything yet. Bob is still in his dressing gown, which means we are both going to need the shower, and time is approaching for us to leave for the meeting. I put my arm around Bob and issue a challenge, first to the shower. He looks flummoxed, then down at his dressing gown. Then he realises what I mean. In a gentlemanly way he puts out his arm and allows me first shot at the shower, with a friendly warning not to use all of the water. Having had a quick lather and rinse I look around for a dry towel. No such luck, all are strewn on the floor in a heap as usual, no change there. I take the end of one and dab myself quickly with a semi dry piece of it.

Oh Lord, can we change our habits? Why do we repeat the same actions day after day, even when we know it is frustrating to others? Is it a subconscious thing? Father break that cycle in me that repeats those habits which I seem unable to do myself.

Bob has a hasty shower too and detects a shortage of dry towels; his answer is to holler at me for a clean one. I find one in the airing cupboard and pass it through to him, with a plea for him to put it on the towel rack afterwards. Well I can always ask. We both dress up for the meeting, Bob in a suit and I in my favourite flowery dress and blazer. Johnny is in his jeans and hoody, I don't make comment as I know he is in a delicate place. It appears that we are ready and on time.

Oh Lord and protector, be our strength and shield.

On arriving at the school we are shown to a room and told that the Head of Year, Mr Hoskins, will be with us in a moment. We sit down and Johnny is shifting around in his seat, obviously nervous. The door opens suddenly and Johnny jumps at the sound. Mr Hoskins extends his right hand and shakes Bob's hand and then mine and introduces himself. He asks what he can do for us and we explain about the rice pudding. Mr Hoskins looks at Johnny and tries to engage him in the conversation, but Johnny finds it embarrassing. When his Head of Year asks Johnny who is responsible, my son, just shrugs his shoulders and looks at the ground. Finally he finds his voice and says loudly and angrily.

'YOU know who it is.'

Mr Hoskins looks stumped.

Johnny continues still surveying the floor, 'Some boys get away with everything in the class. What's the point of me saying who it is as nothing is ever done about it. Anyway, the boy is clever and ropes in others to do his dirty work.'

'Johnny if I knew who it was, I certainly wouldn't let the bullying continue,' Mr Hoskins reassures our son.

Johnny stares long and hard at the man in front of him weighing him up. The revelation he is about to share is not an easy one to divulge. 'You really want to know who it is, are you sure?'

'Of course I do Johnny,' his teacher declares.

Johnny takes a deep breath and sighs, 'It is your son!'

Oh Lord, truth can be an awful shock, especially when it is on your doorstep.

Mr Hoskins looks shocked. He questions Johnny, but he doesn't believe him, that is clearly obvious. Johnny is asked to step outside the door so that we can have a quiet word together. The Head of Year asks me why my son is making up such a story, his son is a quiet lad and he has no hesitation that this sort of behaviour is very uncharacteristic of him. I say that I believe my son; he wouldn't make up this sort of thing. Stalemate! Bob speaks for the first time and says that perhaps we need to speak to someone else as there is a conflict of interest. However, Mr Hoskins emphasises that he wants to be in on the conversation if his son is being accused of bullying. Bob suggests that this should be decided by a third party. Mr Hoskins excuses himself and says that he will be back shortly with another member of staff.

Oh Lord, speaking out can put you at risk, especially if it is an unpopular comment that you make. You Lord know about risk, your preaching was risky. But you did not stop. Father I am cautious about speaking out as it requires courage and I am concerned about the consequences of doing so. Help me not to be afraid when I am called to witness to your glorious Name.

I pop my head out of the room to look for Johnny but he is not there. The corridor is empty and sounds eerily quiet for a school. Thirty minutes pass slowly and still no sign of Johnny nor the Head of Year. Then we hear several footsteps and muffled voices drawing closer to the room. Our son appears at the doorway with an adult, he is dishevelled and miserable. He offers nothing in way of an explanation, just stands there. I take his hand gingerly as I know he is in a catatonic state. The gentleman, who is the school chaplain, speaks to Bob and me in a gentle tone. He tells us that an incident has happened and that he personally wants us to be assured that the matter is being dealt with right now. I must look bemused as the chaplain closes the door and requests us to sit down. Mr Moore explains what has happened. Johnny it seems had gone to the toilet after being asked to go out of the room. It was break time and Johnny had met his friend there and got talking. Then a group of students noticed Johnny outside the facilities and started pushing and kicking him around in an aggressive way. His friend ran off scared that he might be picked on too.

Oh Lord, even your closest friend tried to deny knowing you because he feared for his life.

Then Mr Hoskins had arrived with another teacher quite by accident at the scene, while making his way back to see us. He had broken up the commotion. While Mr Hoskins was dealing with the aftermath he had asked the help of Mr Moore, who had been alerted by the incident, to escort Johnny back to the room we were in and inform us of the situation. The school nurse would also be along soon too.

Oh Lord, sometimes it takes a dramatic incident to make things happen for the best. Father, you saw your son humiliated, scourged, mocked and crucified. You knew that the outcome was worth the sacrifice. May this be the same for us?

The school nurse arrives fairly quickly, but as she tries to suggest that

Johnny go to the medical room for an examination to check if he has incurred any injuries he just cowers and refuses to go. We thank her and she leaves after recommending that we take him to the doctor if we are worried about anything. There is a tap on the door and a very kind lady brings in tea and biscuits for us all. It is a welcome relief for me anyway. Bob asks what happens next and Mr Moore says that we need to wait for Mr Hoskins. Johnny starts to shake and bursts into tears. Bob sits close to him and puts his hand on his knee, trying to reassure him. Mr Moore steps over towards our son too and speaks calmly and with great warmth to him. Johnny slowly breaks out of his inner battle and allows the chaplain to hug him. I feel envious of this moment, but relief at the same time as Johnny is allowing someone, who he seems to care for, to enfold him with his embrace.

Dear Lord, thank you for meeting our needs, for meeting my needs.

There is another knock on the door and Mr Hoskins enters with Mr Oakley, the Head Teacher. He remains silent as his boss shakes hands with Bob and me and then nods at Johnny and says his name, acknowledging him. Mr Oakley gets right to the point and states that he is very unhappy with the events of this morning, and apologises to Johnny for the unpleasant experiences he has had to endure at school. He asks if we want to press charges against the students involved. Bob requests that we have time to think about that and discuss it with Johnny. Mr Oakley continues stating that the students will no longer bully our son and that Johnny was to believe him when he said that. I suddenly remember the vision and the banana incident on the bus and request to know what will happen about the conduct of pupils using school transport. I also bring up the rice pudding incident from yesterday and he assures me that that too will be dealt with very firmly.

Johnny looks up at the Head Teacher and shakily asks, 'What will happen to the students?'

Mr Oakley directs his gaze at Johnny and categorically announces that he will be firm but fair with them.

I can see that Johnny is still worried about something.

72

'But won't they try to get me because I have caused all this trouble?'

The man breathes in and seems to grow an inch taller, making his broad frame even more dominant, he utters one word, 'No'.

I notice Mr Hoskins is surveying his shoes looking extremely uncomfortable and I wonder if he had seen his son during the action he had witnessed earlier.

There is silence, it feels final and is only broken by the chaplain whispering, 'It is over Johnny.'

This made me wonder how long this had all been going on for.

Oh Lord and Head of all outcomes, thank you that it is now over, that responsibility has been accepted, action taken and Justice has triumphed. I pray for those that instigate trauma on others, may they come to know you and become aware of their power to hurt and seek repentance of their crimes.

The Head Teacher offers his hand to us again and says a heartfelt sorry to Johnny. I sense that he is frustrated at not having had the opportunity to sort out the matter before it came to this conclusion. In the mission statement it refers to the school being a safe place to learn, unfortunately this has not been the case for Johnny!

Mr Hoskins also shakes hands but seems unable to do so with eye contact. He looks past Johnny but says, 'I really didn't know.'

They leave the room and the meeting is finished, with Mr Moore, giving us his phone number for us to contact him if we need to. He turns to Johnny and reminds him that his door is always open if he wants a chat. We are accompanied to the school entrance and we all walk out with thoughts occupying our minds.

Oh Lord, thank you that your door is always open and your arms always spread wide.

I think of Mr Hoskins and wonder how he will come to terms with his son's behaviour and what will happen with him now. What drove him to victimise my son? Johnny walks with his hands in his pockets not really looking where he is going. He misses the car and Bob calls him back to reality. Once in the vehicle we all seem to sigh at the same time. Bob tells Johnny that things will get better now and how proud he is of his son's courage to name his tormentor. All Johnny wants however is to leave, to get as far away as possible from this morning's revelation. He is emotionally drained, completely washed out. As if a light has been cut off from its source, Johnny sinks into a deep sleep.

Oh Lord and Lover of Forgiveness, thank you that truth has won this morning. May mercy be shown to those that have been in this conflict and through it a second chance given to all? May all have the courage of the crucified thief to take that second chance and restore the balance of good over evil and inherit the Kingdom of God?

At home I gaze at my son's peaceful state on the back seat of the car. Bob and I decide to leave him where he is and find a duvet to cover him. It has been an emotional morning. A rush of heady relief fills my body and the quiet of our house feels incredibly comforting. All of a sudden I burst into tears and an uncontrollable flood cascades down my cheeks onto my clothing. Bob comes and embraces me, he too has a tear stained face.

Oh Lord, we are awash with tears of relief.

And at this moment God embraces us both and whispers:

I am with you always.

Afternoon Prayer

Both Bob and I decide that Johnny ought to go and see the doctor as we don't know the state of his injuries, both psychologically and physically. Bob calls the surgery and they are amenable to the situation, so with Johnny still asleep on the back seat of the car, the pair head off to see the doctor.

Oh Lord, the mind is a precious and delicate product of your artistic nature. It shapes the colour of our days and nights. It is the subject of amazing insights and great depths of despair, both poles of the same canvas. It has the ability to transform our day or to threaten a storm from the dark clouds of confusion and anxiety, a white to black spectrum with the colours of the rainbow in between. It takes Your Holy Spirit to activate the full dimension of its powerful source. So often I only see the outline, black and white, please Father fill in the negative of my photo with your glorious colours.

With a dearly needed cup of tea, I sit down on the sofa; my mind awash with the morning's disclosures. The nectar of my favourite brew fills my senses and I slowly begin to reflect on God's help during the first half of the day. Within the calmness of my Father's spirit I enter my favourite resting place. The world behind the waterfall, my sanctuary from this world's manic pace. I walk over the bridge and wave to my daughter, who is happily playing with her friends in the shallow waters of peace. My angel, who God took to himself so many years ago, my first child Libby had been born in a rush, too early to breathe this life's air. She had been greatly anticipated being our first baby, but for some reason at twenty one week's her entry into our world had been swift and traumatic. There was no medical explanation as to why Libby had been rejected by my body, she just was and now God had the pleasure of her company as she played happily with all the other angels in His playground.

Come my love, I am waiting for you.

The waterfall is so beautiful; it cascades down and spills over into the pool of refreshment. I stand under it, allowing the shower to wash me clean. The Angel hands me a new white garment and a purple sash and

75

accompanies me to the Father's Kingdom. Jesus is already waiting for me with his arms outstretched, longing to see and hug me.

Oh my child, how good it is to see you. How beautiful you are my joy, my love.

Tears of happiness flow from my eyes. My Lord, my God, my Saviour, how I adore you. Your hugs uplift and heal me, I am yours. My deliverer holds me away from him so that he can look into my eyes. His gaze is all consuming.

I love you.

The wave of Love is almost overwhelming, but he holds back his true complete passion for me, otherwise I would be totally overpowered. I am not ready for His world, not yet. I am not in the transformed state of light capable of such exposure to His Source of Love.

I love you too.

We walk hand in hand, and Jesus shows me his incredible world. The colours are like nothing I have seen before; the jewels are sparkling and reflecting His glory. Angels are singing the most glorious anthems. There such a joy in the freedom of feeling nothing but peace and extreme happiness as I walk with my Lover. I know that I am adored by Him passionately and this is truly awesome beyond words. Time is nothing here; everything is just Love and an expression of that Love.

I have a gift for you my precious one.

Jesus stands facing me and asks one of the angels to open the box that he holds. My master takes out a belt with a buckle and puts it around my waist, then a breast plate, shoes, a shield, helmet and last of all a sword.

My delight, this is the Armour of my Father. My gift to you, to enable you to stand and be strong in His mighty power, in the world of man that is ruled by the evil one.

76

Thank you my Lord. It is magnificent.

The gift is beautiful, each item spectacularly crafted with inlaid jewels. It is a wonderfully light material that is both immensely strong and so incredibly delicate that it fits snugly and seems to mould into the very sinews of my being. It is like nothing I have ever seen before. I stand in awe of these heavenly creations.

Wear it always my treasure.

I will my love.

We continue our walk in silence just enjoying our time together and taking in the Love of the Kingdom. A host of Angels are worshipping in song over the brow of a hill and we go and join them. They are encircling a prayer and praise meeting somewhere on earth, uniting with the celebrants in their joyful response to God. The joint effect illuminates the Kingdom and everyone embraces the glorification. What a celebration. I want to stay forever.

My beauty, come and join the party.

I sing and praise God, it is all so natural. I am ablaze with the song of the angels. The power overflows from the Heavenly place and showers down on the earthly meeting. People fall in the Spirit, awash with His Love. Now I know why these gatherings are so powerful. The Praise continues as we slowly draw away.

My joy, it has been a pleasure to have your company. Please come again soon. I love you so very much.

Oh Lord, do I have to go?

I am always close; never doubt that, my adorable love.

God's Spirit leaves me and suddenly I am aware that the surrounding has changed. My tea is still hot and waiting to be drunk. I feel greatly refreshed. My God how awesome you are. I drink in the peace and sip my tea. If only everyone knew of Your wonders, could experience Your timeless world, how they would long to be in Your presence. The telephone catches me off guard, its tone calling my attention to matters of this world. Before I manage to pick the receiver up it rings off. I dial the free number to see who was calling, but the caller withheld their number. I shrug and think that if it is important they will ring again. Apparently it is important as the phone starts again, but there is silence as I pick up the receiver. I request an answer to my hello, but nothing. I speak to the silence, as I have a feeling that it is my father. He finally answers, asking who I am. A wave of heaviness hangs over my response. My dad is having one of those days, when confusion rules his mind.

I suggest he puts my mother on the telephone and I can hear him say, 'It's for you.'

Oh Lord, you were fortunate never to suffer old age in this world. It appears cruel and undignified when the mind is attacked by disease. That spark taken away and dull responses cloud an intelligent past. Slowly recognition of loved ones fades and a dark emptiness sucks in the memories of a lifetime. I am frightened of growing old Father.

My parents live further away than I would like. I cannot just pop in the car and see them for an hour or two as it is a two hundred mile round trip. My mother is marvellous the way she copes with dad's condition. She laughs his antics off as though they were part of a comedy show. Her voice very rarely gives away her pain, but I am sure that if I could see her eyes they would tell another story. Mum comes to the phone; she is sprightly in her manner. I ask if all is well with my father and she tells me that dad had an interesting walk in the early hours of this morning in his birthday suit. He had gone to the post office to collect a delivery. Apparently I had sent him a present! He had woken up the proprietor and given her an awful shock. She had rung the police and they, knowing my father, had brought him home covered in a blanket. He had been very upset at not being able to get the parcel. My mum, a great innovator, had wrapped up a shoe box when my dad was back in bed fast asleep, and placed it by the front door behind the flower pot for him to find later. He had wanted to thank me, but forgot what it was I had sent him and that was the reason he had rung me.

Oh Lord, how often I am forgetful? Sometimes it is because I don't want to remember and other times it is simply that there is too much to think about. Father help me to remember what I need to and not to forget what is important.

My mum, I feel, is one of the modern day saints, a modern day holy person. We are all called to be saints, to be holy in a practical way, in what we do, say and think, but not in a self-righteous way. My mum is doing what is right for my father and in doing so is honouring God. I am sure that her love in their marriage will be celebrated with many blessings from the Father. I am not sure that I could live her witness of love day in day out.

Oh Lord, help me to be holy in the little things so that when the big call comes I will be ready and willing to give honour to God.

I can hear that my mum is distracted and tell her that I will ring again soon. There is a crash just before she puts the telephone down.

'Fred I wouldn't stick that up there.'

There was silence followed by the purr of the tone. The mind boggles as to what my father was about to do, but no doubt my mother will have it under control in a matter of minutes. I do wonder how much longer my mum can cope with the bizarre actions of my dad.

Oh Lord, how proud my father was once. He would be so upset if he knew of his actions now. Thank you that he cannot see the present tangle of his life.

The key turns in the lock and Bob and Johnny step into the hallway. My son makes his way up to his bedroom, his place of sanctuary. We retire to the sitting room and Bob tells me that Johnny will need some time off from school. There are no bones broken, lots of painful bruising, but it is the impact of all the bullying that concerns the doctor. Bob continues and tells me that Johnny will be referred for counselling as soon as possible. I know that this is the right thing to do for our son; I just hope the NHS is quick about the referral. Bob decides to ring the school and let them know the doctor's instructions.

Oh Lord, bruises will fade in time but words can be like cancer eating away at the core of one's being. Your word brought forth LIFE. In the beginning was the Word, and the Word was with God, and the Word was God. Father, help my words bring forth life and may any signs of word cancer be eradicated by the blood of the cross.

Bob has already decided that he will either arrange time off or work from home so that he can be with Johnny and support him. I am so grateful for his support in this. We hold each other's hand for a shared moment.

Oh Lord, together we are strong.

In this precious silence I hear a sound behind the sofa that we are sitting on, a kind of scratching. I turn to Bob to see if he is aware of this noise. He has his eyes closed so I assume that he hasn't heard anything. The noise starts again.

'Can you hear that Bob?' I ask.

He answers, 'What?'

Sometimes I question his hearing, but then with four children he can't be blamed for auditory selection. I suggest that we pull the sofa out to check the cause of the scratching. We heave together and then kneel on the cushions and peep over the top of the settee. There trying to tunnel through the skirting board is a little field mouse. A present no doubt brought in at some point by our cat. Slowly and carefully we both take either end of the three-seater and approach with caution trying not to scare the little rodent. It freezes, I am sure that it is staring at me intently. Both of us move in with our hands cupped to catch it, it moves so fast that we bang heads together and the mouse escapes under the sofa.

Oh Lord, united we stand.

Our pet feline arrives on the scene; she jumps onto Bob's back to see what we are looking at. Cat senses are alerted, she slinks down to the exact place the creature had darted under. Her ears pricked up, tail erect, ready to thrust a paw towards the prey. But Bob has other plans, he scoops her up and takes her into the kitchen and closes the door, leaving her to mew frantically at the injustice of being taken out of the action. Bob decides on a strategic plan of action. He will lift up the sofa and I will grab the intruder. Easier said than done! As soon as he erects the furniture the mouse goes further towards the end that is still on the ground. I can't physically get under that part and Bob is yelling at me to be quick. He lowers the settee hoping that I have done my job. As quickly as he can he moves to the other end of the sofa and picks it up, and tells me to capture the rodent. But there is no sign of it.

Oh Lord, I sense that this is one of your lighter moments, reminding me that you never chase us but wait for us to come to you freely, giving us that free choice.

The hunt begins and Bob decides that maybe he should use the one thing that will search out and find the little creature, Bonny our cat. As soon as Bob opens the kitchen door our feline friend shoots into the sitting room ready for action. Her nose to the ground, eyes alert, checking the last place she had seen her prey. She listens, nothing, and then moves on. Carefully like a tracker she stealthily homes in on the weaker species. She pounces, catches and then proudly deposits an imitation stuffed toy mouse at Bob's feet. Not quite what we are hoping for, but in the right direction I suppose. However Bonny thinks it is a game and taunts and flips the toy with great satisfaction. Then Bob takes it off her and throws it across the room, it lands just in front of the television. As Bonny goes for it she suddenly stops, there in front of her is the real thing hiding under the TV stand. They eye one another up and down.

Oh Lord, sometimes I think we do the same, eye you up and down before we are sure we can trust what we see. We might think 'are you for real'? Then there is the uncertainty of what you will ask of us/of me. Father, how suspicious we are, expecting terms and conditions instead of your unconditional love.

It is a standoff, which Bob uses to his advantage, he moves quicker than I have seen in years and swipes the field mouse in his hand in one swift movement. Bonny is so surprised that she crawls under the stand to see where the tiny animal has gone. She is beside herself, frantically searching, jumping over wires and controllers, in an effort to find her prey. Meanwhile seeing that Bonny is occupied Bob takes the little bundle of fluff outside to a safe corner of the garden.

81

Oh Lord, thank you that I am safe in your hands. That I have been ever since you thought of me. I love your psalm 139, how could I ever believe having read that, that my life is just random. How awesome that I am in your hands and will always be to the end of time.

Our sudden furore now over, we laugh about the ingenuity of the field mouse in evading capture. I rub my head and Bob does too from when we clashed and we just fall about laughing. It is like a breath of fresh air, our release. And then I feel a sudden rush propelling itself from the depths of my being, like a volcanic eruption. I cannot stop the outburst, the explosion of tears that pour out from my soul. I sob uncontrollably and Bob wraps his arms around me once again and allows the torrent of fluid to soak his shirt forming a wet imprint around his heart.

Oh Lord, God of my heart, soul and mind. Hug me as Bob is doing now. I just need that closeness right now.

The moment of anguish is over and I take a deep breath. Life has to go on, there are things to do, a cake to bake, tea to prepare. Bob asks if I am alright and kisses me on the cheek, reassuring me that when you are on the bottom rung of the ladder the only way is up. I am so grateful for his wisdom, for his companionship on my journey, on our journey through life.

Oh Lord, The Deep to deep calls, The Voice to the voice of the waters of your fountains. All your storms and your waves passed over me. (Aramaic Bible in Plain English 2010)

I feel uplifted because the God of my Life, the Rock of my salvation has not forgotten me, He does not desert nor deny me, because he is my mercy, truth, power and refuge.

Oh Lord, I praise and thank you. I glorify Your Holy Name. Nothing can compare with you; I am humbled in your Sight. Magnificent Maker, Almighty Godhead. I worship you.

I decide to bake a chocolate cake, Johnny's favourite. Then I wonder if he has eaten anything today or even had a drink? Surely he has, but then again he refused breakfast, so I ask Bob to make a sandwich and to take up some juice as well for our son. Bob returns with the sandwich but the drink has been accepted. The cake doesn't take long to whip up and pop into the oven. Next I put a load of washing on; I am surprised no one has hollered for clean underwear as the basket with dirties in, is still in the bathroom where I left it yesterday. I decide on a stir fry for our meal, and do the preparation now so that when the anthem of 'I am hungry' is sung the response will be 'Food is on its way'.

Oh Lord, our needs are simple, food, water, love, warmth, physical comfort, clothing, and a healthy environment. All things that we take for granted when our world is secure. Each need being crafted, to form firm foundation stones, on which to build a strong and healthy person. But all of these needs are nothing without you as the ultimate source, the centre of the need. Only you can fulfil these needs completely. Without You I am no more than a gong booming or a cymbal clashing.

The telephone rings and just as I am about to pick up the receiver, having launched myself full speed from the kitchen to the house phone in the hallway, it stops. Then it starts again. I swipe it up as quickly as I can, and announce my number and say a hearty 'hello'. It is Cathy. I change my tone to a more sombre one and ask how she is. She says that she feels better now as the hospital is going to give James the help he needs. It will take time but things are moving in the right direction. She thanks me for my support and hopes that I will be able to pop round soon to have a coffee with her. I am struggling as I am not sure when I can in fact do this and I don't want to disappoint her when she is in a fragile state. Being torn isn't a nice feeling, and I know that she would understand if I told her about our situation at present with Johnny. But I still can't help feeling I am letting her down. I suggest that perhaps tomorrow afternoon might be a good time if she is free then. We leave the arrangement like that as the front door explodes open.

'Hello mum,' my three children call out at once.

I hastily say goodbye to Cathy, she can hear the commotion and knows that I need to go. I feel like I am running a marathon through life!

Oh Lord, help me to run with endurance the race set forth for me.

Each hugs me and then awaits an account of the morning's meeting. I would rather discuss it over tea and suggest that they pop up and see Johnny while I get it ready. I encourage them not to push him for details as he is vulnerable at the moment. Lily Pink asks what I mean, and Henry takes her by the hand and says that it means, being fragile like a flower. She understands and says, 'Ok.'

They all clamber up the stairs and file into Johnny's room. I hear the creak of his bed and imagine them all sitting crowded on the side and edge of it. If they are talking it is quietly as I cannot hear anything more through the kitchen ceiling.

Oh Lord, how good and pleasant it is when brothers and sisters live together in unity!

Lay your unity at the foot of the Trinity Vicki; there you will receive my Grace.

Evening Prayer

The stir fry is a success and even Johnny comes down for a little and eats his meal with us all. He woofs down the chocolate cake, asking for seconds. Once he has escaped back to his room Bob and I start the conversation about the morning's events. All listen intently, upset about Johnny's experience. Then Henry and Gabby tell us that the whole school had to attend an assembly in the afternoon where the Headmaster rammed home the zero tolerance procedure towards bullying. After that there were rumours which stated that the five boys involved had been taken to the headmaster's office after the incident and from there sent home. Henry tells us that Mr Hoskins's son was one of them.

Oh Lord, this confirmation saddens me.

Lily Pink looks on with wide eyes and takes it all in. She asks what will happen with Johnny now. Will he go back to school? We reassure her that Johnny with all our help will be alright, and that we must support him if he feels down and not able to cope at times. Gabby asks the age old question of why and finds it hard that Isaac Hoskins was part of such actions. Then it dawns on her that he was subjected to bullying when it was found out that his father was a teacher at the school. The bullied became the bully. She looks down and contemplates this thought and announces that Isaac needs our forgiveness and prayers. Henry snorts and says that if Isaac crosses his path he will give him what for.

Oh Lord, an eye for an eye might give us more satisfaction in the early stages of anger, but it doesn't solve anything and is likely to make things worse. You taught forgiveness as the solution, but how hard this lesson is. How hard it is to teach our children. I look at your cross and see that there is no other way; only through this medium can we be saved. Father help me to forgive with outstretched arms.

Gabby is right we have to forgive, and I need to pray that my children will embrace this answer too. Henry can be hot headed but it is usually in defence of his siblings or in response to an injustice caused by an unfair authority. Fairness to him is equality, all being equal and having the same rights no matter who you are. His enthusiasm comes from his

85

youth, from the pureness that he can make a difference. But sometimes in his frustration a threat of a punch or a kick might be the solution when nothing else appears to be working.

Oh Lord, I am hot headed at times; frustration will act first and common sense afterwards. Hind sight is a wonderful thing, but can come at a price. Father, when my anger rages, don't let the storm cloud my judgement.

Before we end our conversation at the dinner table we decide as a family to take this opportunity to offer up the needs of the day. I place the boys who it appears have been suspended and their families to our Father's care. Gabby mentions our own intentions. Lily Pink asks for Johnny to get better soon. Henry says Amen and Bob prays protection for us all as head of the family. There is a brief silence and then plates start to rattle as the dishes are piled up and taken into the kitchen. All three children do the washing up and putting away without being asked or nagged to.

Oh Lord, thank you for this precious moment.

There is a knock on the front door and Gabby rushes to open it. Four of her friends pile in and kick off their footwear. One of them is holding a scruffy looking shoe that she found on the tarmac outside our house. It looks like mine so I take it off her and put it in the utility room to deal with later.

Oh Lord, I forgot my fouled shoe, just like I forget to do those little things that bug me so. Leaving it can't be so bad can it?

Gabby informs me that her friends have come round to do their maths homework. The fourteen year olds are all taller than me and I appreciate their manners in calling me Mrs S. On one of their previous visits I suggested that they called me Vicki, but all refused on the grounds that I deserved to be addressed correctly. So Mrs S became the norm. I pop my head around the sitting room door and see that they have made themselves at home. Jenny, the oldest of the bunch looks at me with fluttering eyelids and asks if I can bake some little cakes for them to eat while they do their homework.

'You are the queen of the Sponges after all!'

Oh Lord, how wonderful that these teenagers feel so comfortable in my house to be able to ask for their needs. In Your presence I feel the same Father.

I love baking and doing this treat is not a chore at all. I know how gratefully this little act will be received. There is nothing like fresh hot cakes straight from the oven. As soon as they are ready the girls pounce on them in delight. I notice however, that not a lot of homework seems to be going on. There is laughter, lots of high jinks and in the middle of it all, Lily Pink appears to be entertaining them with her magic tricks. I enquire about homework and they say it is in the process of being done! At which point Johnny walks down the stairs with a sheet of paper with what looks like some equations on it.

He hands it to Gabby. 'All done' he says and heads upstairs again. I call after him. He turns and smiles and shrugs his shoulders. 'They couldn't do it so Gabs asked me to help.'

I just say thanks and enquire how he is doing; he folds his arms around himself and quietly says, 'Ok I think'.

I respond with an 'I Love You' and he lowers his head and nods it up and down.

'You too,' he whispers.

I feel giddy with his response. It has been a while since he has been able to say those words. He shoots off quickly back to his bedroom.

Oh Lord, thank you. This little message is an enormous present, a glimmer of a greater source of radiance hidden within an enclosed world. Just as you are only able to show us a fraction of your Glory, due to our human nature, it sometimes makes me giddy. How amazing, how awesome will be the day when I experience your full radiance.

With the girls occupied, Henry and Johnny in their rooms and Bob rummaging through his past photos, I feel a strong urge to put pen to paper. I retire to my bedroom where it is a little quieter and write:

87

Dear Johnny,

You mean the world to me. When you were born I gazed on your little body fighting for life, wanting to live. We spent many hours, you and I in the Special Care Baby Unit, I watching the beeps, you listening to them on the monitors. No one thought you would survive. But I did, I always knew you were a fighter.

I would bring Gabby to see you and put her hand into the incubator to touch yours so that you still had that contact with her that you had in the womb. The pings would go quicker and I knew you were aware of her presence. We couldn't do it for long as you needed a steady flow of warmth and oxygen around you. Then when you stopped breathing I rocked you gently to remind you that you needed to breathe. I needed you to breathe. I couldn't bear losing you. I loved you so much. I still do.

I know, my precious young man that you find touch and eye contact difficult, that understanding people is hard for you, especially when emotions are present. But that doesn't matter to me. I love you as you are. Your insight into things always intrigues me, and your desire to be a scientist is wonderful. I know you will make it as you are a talented and brave person. Hold onto your dreams and don't let anyone take them away from you. Your life is precious and you have an important role to play in it. I am here for you no matter what, in your struggles and in your accomplishments. We stand together you and me. Your family too love you and are united in wanting only the very best for you, because you are who you are. You are not alone; we are all here for you. I am here for you, and always will be. I will never stop loving you and wanting the best for you. You are special, authentic and unique. You are my son and you are adored. Never forget that.

I so want to cuddle you, to cradle you at times when I see your pain, but I understand your individuality and am prepared to wait for your willingness to accept this gesture from me. My heart will always be open to you.

I am so proud of you my son,

With my love

Mum

I slip the letter under Johnny's door. I have said what I wanted to say.

Oh Lord, you have written us a love story, telling us how much you love us and are prepared to wait for our movement towards your Kingdom. How often do we read it, understand it, acknowledge it, act on it, believe it, truly believe it, and allow it to become a part of us. Please Father; open my eyes to your love story today.

I hear the joyous racket from the sitting room; it is so good to hear. It makes me smile. I knock and wait for the call to say that it is alright for me to enter. As I do I trip over Bonny, the cat, who is desperate to get out of the bedlam and fall unceremoniously towards Jenny and Lucy. They catch and prevent me from hurtling down to the ground.

'Enjoy your trip?' I hear Gabby say.

I chuckle and express that the trip was unexpected but interesting. Having collected myself I look around the room. All the cakes have been eaten, homework copied, and Lily Pink is lying on the floor in a mummified state. As I look rather perplexed Gabby informs me that they are doing an experiment for science. Lily Pink seems to think that being totally enfolded in toilet paper is a great honour. A face, boobs, tummy button and toenails have been drawn on. I can't help but think it very funny. They help LP get up and turn on some music and encourage her to dance. Lily Pink doesn't need any further promptings and has everyone in hysterics attempting to do an Egyptian dance movement. The toilet paper starts to unwind due to the actions. Mobile phones are produced to take a picture, no doubt for a Facebook windup later.

Oh Lord, thank you for humour; it really makes my day, especially the humour of the young which is free and not frightened to express itself.

All of a sudden a serious expression forms on Lily Pink's face. She utters an urgent request.

'What time does Munday's close?'

I suggest that it might be eight o'clock and she tells me that she needs an orange tutu for tomorrow. I remind my daughter that she has a

89

yellow, blue and white tutu, were none of these any good? She gives me the look, obviously not. I glance at the time and it says seven. I ask Lily Pink when she knew about this and she states, last week. It doesn't surprise me. Fortunately Munday is only fifteen minutes away by car and stocks all sorts of weird and wonderful things. I suggest that we go now and LP heads for the door. Gabby looks at Lily Pink and asks if she is going dressed up as a mummy. She heads over to her sister and they start pulling at the tissue paper. It ends up everywhere in small pieces. These are then grabbed and made into snow balls and a fight ensues. Once Lily Pink is outside the room I close the door with a hopeful statement that all will be cleared up before I get back!

Oh Lord, Mayhem! There must have been great confusion when you were arrested: your disciples and other factions meeting together, your friend, also known to both sides kissing and betraying you, Simon Peter drawing a sword and cutting off an ear of a high priest's slave, your healing of the severed ear, your arrest. What chaos, fear, utter bewilderment, but you say "Shall I not drink from the cup of suffering the Father has given me?" You tell your followers that you know what you are doing. You try to reassure them, but most of them run off. I sometimes wonder if I would do the same, would I have the courage to stay close by you. Father how comforting it is that you know what you are doing.

Bob decides suddenly that he will come with us. He sits in the passenger seat and Lily Pink in the back. I always feel that I am undergoing my driving test again when Bob is beside me not driving. He can't help himself and feels he has to comment on every manoeuvre I make. He reminds me to put my lights on, as if I would forget! Mind the speed camera; I am doing thirty miles an hour! Signal right, well I wouldn't signal left if I was going right! Watch the lorry coming in the other direction; I am on the other side of the road, what is the problem? I don't think he realises how annoying it is. I have been driving longer than he and had fewer crashes. Even the kids think I am the better driver. It must be a man thing.

Oh Lord, trust is an amazing gift to have. Help me to trust in you so that the worries of everyday life are put into perspective.

The shop is still open so my guess was right. We go straight to the tutus and put an orange one into our basket. Bob has disappeared and is not

90

in view anywhere. There is an area with hats, I love hats, but unfortunately they don't like me. All seem to be a one size fit and in my case that means big. Lily Pink loves it when I try them on, so to amuse ourselves until Bob shows up again I do exactly that. There is a lovely red cocktail hat that fits easily over my head and down past my eyes, all I would need to do is cut out two holes so that I can see. The purple wide brim hat totally immerses my head and I can swivel it around with no problem (the hat that is!). The white pill box hat with its frills just sits on my head and would need a whole can of hair spray to keep it from blowing away. Alternatively I could tie a ribbon all around it like a bandage! Lily Pink passes me a straw hat and just clutches her stomach with laughter as I put it on and can literally submerge myself in its vastness as it sinks down to my shoulders.

'Now I like that one,' Bob intones, 'goes with the colour of your shoes.'

Well let's face it that's about all you would see if I wore this one.

Oh Lord, I know that I am not the average size for the normal person, as advertised by the media. My head is too small, my bottom too big, my feet tiny, and my boobs don't look full, but droop towards my stomach. I am no model, haven't been air brushed in a photo shoot to look wonderful and contrived, to convince the younger generation that being without blemish is the new black. I am me, warts and all, take me or leave me, but at least everything is genuine. Apart from my dyed hair of course! Father what you see is what you get and I can't hoodwink you.

Bob is carrying something in a carrier bag; he tries to hide it behind his back. I ask if he found anything worth buying and he tries to dismiss my question with a stuttered 'no, not really'. I don't push it as he obviously wishes to keep it secret for the time being. We go and pay for the tutu and head back home, with the usual, mind that parked car, the traffic light is red, there is a car pulling out from the side road, and watch the pedestrian walking on the pavement! I have to laugh at that one as I thought that that was where they are supposed to walk. If only Bob knew how silly he sounds. Who needs a sat nav, when I can have an irritating voice right next to me?

Oh Lord, give me my husband any day; he's a laugh a minute.

91

The girls are on their way out when we arrive back home. There are cars parked all over the cul de sac, some brand new, others like ours, ancient, (meaning more than five years old) waiting with engines running to pick up the teenagers. We have to wait as our drive is blocked; all girls give me an air kiss through the open car window and thank me for the cakes. I say come again as it is always lovely to see and hear them. I ask did they tidy up.

'Yes Mrs S,' they all say.

Gabby waves them goodbye and indicates for them to message her soon! We pull in and lock the car. Gabby has disappeared so Lily Pink runs off to find and show her the new tutu. There is an argument about Gabby wanting to try it on, but Lily Pink doesn't want her to as she will stretch it. Finally silence prevails when Bob goes and tells them to pack it in. The carrier bag he was holding has been put somewhere. So the mystery remains as to what is in it.

Oh Lord, you are a mystery, a conundrum that people and scientists have tried to fathom from the beginning of time. But you are not hidden, only to the eyes of the non-believer. Thank you Father for my faith as it is a gift. May I never lose it?

I hear Lily Pink bang the bedroom door and stomp off into our room so I venture upstairs to see Gabby. I want to ask her why she had got Johnny to do her homework when she is top of her class for maths. Gabby is lying on her bed, and she motions for me to sit on it. I ask my question and she tells me that she wanted Johnny to feel good and needed. The best way she knew how was to get him to share his knowledge, so she thought she would ask him to help her friends, even though she knew the answers herself. It seemed to work she said, as he came down later to see if they had understood his workings out and how he had come to calculate the answers. Her friends had asked him to sit with them and he had for a little while in the middle of all the discarded toilet roll! Gabby knew that Lucy was sweet on Johnny and would make him feel comfortable in their company, without him knowing her feelings for him. She had asked him to explain one of the maths questions and he had come alive with the theory. Gabby was surprised that when he left the room he turned around and said that he was happy to help them anytime. As she said this her face produced an enormous proud smile remembering her brother's achievement. Only she among her friends knew what courage this took for Johnny to share his world.

Oh Lord, how wonderful when we understand the complexity of another's world and just accept that a simple request can mean so much to that other person. Help me to remember that a little kindness and understanding goes a long way in building up a broken soul.

I am so proud of Gabby, she just knew what button to press to make her brother respond and connect again with the world of man. Gabby is her brother's best therapist, she knows him so well, she knows how he ticks. Although not from the same egg, they were taken from the same clay and moulded together by the Father and given the same breath of life.

Oh Lord, our souls are yours, may they never depart from you. You are the potter, I am the clay. You formed me, took a jewel from your crown, planted it deep within my being, and gave me your spirit so that I can call upon you in the reverence of your presence.

I go to give Gabby a hug and she lets me. I inhale the beauty of this moment and close my eyes to allow the full force to penetrate my being. I know that she wants to get back to her chat session, so I smile at her and leave the room. As I do, I hear my name being called from Johnny's room. Inside he is holding my letter. He looks up at me awkwardly, and hands me a letter in return. He asks me to take it away and read it quietly without anyone else around and then says that there is no need to reply. The quietest place in the house at this moment is the downstairs toilet. As no one is in the little room I enter and lock the door.

Oh Lord of miracles, thank you.

Slowly I open the letter and read:

Dear mum,

I am sorry for the things I said to you. I don't hate you; I just get so angry inside with myself for being me. I don't understand who I am,

93

but thank you for your love, for knowing my limitations and accepting them.

I feel like I am serving a life term in prison. I see you standing out of reach, I try to reach you but my body and mind are trapped behind the bars. I stretch my arm as far as possible but the bars prevent me from reaching you, from hugging you and showing my true feelings. I am a prisoner unable to escape the cell of my disability.

I long to be free to express my inner self, to be part of your world, to join in and be like everyone else. I hate being different, trapped in a parallel world, a world that is alien to you and the family, seeing, but unable to partake. There is no key, not even a lock to put a key in, no release.

I am a reluctant prisoner, confined indefinitely, with no reprieve date. What heinous crime have I committed to be serving this sentence? How do I find freedom?

I may not show it but I do love you, I always have.

Thanks for hanging in there for me.

Johnny

I hold the letter to my heart. What a revelation from my son and how disturbing too. His life seen as a prisoner, locked forever in an inescapable fortress of the mind, certainly not by choice. But unknown to him he has found a slit, a chink in the iron, a route out. For the very first time I am able to see his world from his side of the door. There might not be a lock with a keyhole in it, but he has opened it fractionally with a pen.

Oh Lord, you understand about being a prisoner, charged as a criminal and sentenced without being guilty. You rose above it all. Help me to mirror your example to help my son to be who you made him to be.

I am struck by the simplicity of the solution. Paper doesn't present a threat, however sharing the words on it do. I am so grateful that he has had the desire to try and express his experiences through this medium. It is a significant move on his part.

Oh Lord what a blessing, thank you.

And God met with me in the smallest room and said:

Vicki nothing is set in stone. With Me everything is possible for those that believe. Remember life was never meant to be easy, but with Me you will always have a helping hand and a back that will carry you when you can't walk anymore.

Night Prayer

It has been a hard journey today, but there have been laughs as well as drama enacted during the hours of sunlight and sunset. There have been victories and revelations, all of which have made a colourful scene of threads intertwining with each other to form a spectacular landscape of life.

Oh Lord, this day has been full of truths, some painful as well as revealing. I have witnessed betrayal and denial, disbelief and disaccreditation, sorrow and justice. Today I stood by my son who has been offered up on a dish of humiliation to the world. I heard the words of forgiveness and saw the opening of a brave new era. I sense your hand in all of this Father.

Indeed my hand was very close to your experience Vicki, because you said 'yes' today, to be with me in the Olive Grove. To stand by me as I was betrayed and arrested for doing my Father's Will. You did not run away, but stood close by, I felt your love.

I did not want to go through such turmoil, to see my son abused and shamed by his peers. A mother's heart wants only the best for her offspring, for them to be happy and confident, able to live and learn in safety. Why was it necessary for my son to be singled out and tormented, a soul that has not deserved it?

Vicki, my dearest one, no one deserves this treatment, that is why I allowed the guards to arrest me, to take me away without a fight. The wickedness of this world has no power over me because I willingly went forth to my destiny.

But Johnny didn't willingly ask to be bullied.

No he did not; Satan overcame the minds of the weak, bribed and turned them away promising status and kingship of this world. But Good has prevailed from this situation, did not Forgiveness show his head, and a meeting of minds begin to open up. Ever present was Victory, Strength and Power to build up and mend the broken hearted. Remember Vicki I AM in all things, but not in the sin.

96

I ponder all of this in my heart. This has been an awesome day.

Oh Lord, how intertwined our journey is, if only we could see that connection more readily. Thank you for your closeness today my love, my Saviour.

Sleep in my love Vicki.

Chapter Four

Thursday

Morning Prayer

'The Spirit himself testifies with our spirit that we are God's children, then we are heirs-heirs of God and co-heirs with Christ, if indeed we share in his sufferings in order that we may also share in his glory.' - Paul of Tarsus; Romans 8:16-17 (New International Version)

I am woken by a lot of crashing and banging coming from Henry's room, he seems agitated about something. I look at my alarm clock and see that it is six o'clock in the morning, early for Henry. I pull the duvet off and venture to look around his bedroom door. He is half under his bed.

'Lost anything in particular Henry?' I enquire.

'My boots,' he answers.

I wonder which boots, and scan quickly around his self-induced mess. I spot a blue strip and ask if he means his football boots. He replies in the affirmative. I suggest that I might know where they are and he moves fairly rapidly back from under his bed. Thinking he has cleared the wooden frame he starts to lift his head up and crunches it on the base. I wince as it sounded quite painful. He rubs the area that hurts and looks at me with a frown.

'So where do you think they are?' he intones trying not to sound in too much pain.

I ask if he checked his floor first, he looks annoyed at my suggestion, then follows my pointed finger. He sighs showing visible traces of frustration.

'I have already looked there.'

Rather than further my son's obvious awkwardness, I step over the pile of dirty clothing and dishes and produce from under a pair of trunks his blue and black pair of boots. He looks and me and says thank you. They are covered in dried mud. He moans as he knows that he should have cleaned them after the last match. Without a moment's thought he bangs them together there and then and sprays the dirt all over the place. I look on in disbelief.

Oh Lord, it isn't even half past six and the madness of the day has started. I sense this is going to be another one of those days!

I try to brace myself, but the noise and the discharging black earth matter flying all over the place sparks a volcanic eruption.

'Henry, for crying out loud, not in your bedroom!'

He stops, suddenly aware of the silence. The escalation of anger changes in an instance and becomes a gush of sobs, tears pouring out of my eyes and down my pyjamas. At this moment I am joined by the entire household, everyone talking at once wanting to know what is going on. I push through the throng and close the door to my bedroom with a firm hand. It is a sign to everyone not to venture in.

Oh Lord, I can't talk right now as I am so angry.

I sit on the edge of my bed and wonder about my life. I don't want to say 'Yes' today, I am so fed up with struggling. I feel like I am on trial, but why and for what? I have tried to bring up my family with codes of conduct, morals and a thought for their parents and siblings. So where has it gone wrong? Why am I being tried like this? Do I not have a right to be respected, does our home deserve to look like it has been burgled, ransacked by teenagers, used as a dumping ground by adults? Why do I feel judged by its condition, by others, even by myself? I feel culpable even though I am not solely to blame. How is it that others manage to do all the housework chores, go to work, raise a family, be a confidante, supporter and lover and still look like they could run a marathon at the end of the day. Is this life my sentence? Guilty even though I am innocent?

99

Vicki, I have not judged you.

Not now Lord, I can't take your call.

I cannot hear anything from the hallway outside. I assume everyone has gone to prepare for school. I take a really big breath and breathe out trying to calm myself. There is a faint tap at the door. I ignore it. It repeats, and again I ignore it. The third time, I get up off the bed and open the door. It is Johnny. My face must look awful but he just embraces me. I suddenly realise that his arms are around me and I feel a lump in my throat. There are no words. My son is trying to console me, to reach out to me. He has touched the untouchable. I am truly humbled by his gesture. Then he retreats and I am left with my thoughts.

Oh Lord, how did you know how to reach me? You used the most fragile flower in my garden to cajole me. Thank you for your passionate affection, for not giving up on me.

Vicki, I have not judged you. I have seen your efforts, you are amazing, and no one knows the degree by which you try apart from me. You choose to follow me, that is what is important, not the external facade. All that will pass away one day, but your soul is what will be presented at the final judgement not your household skills. Be gentle on yourself, my love.

But it is the lack of common sense, the immediate solution that doesn't register the bigger problem that the thoughtless action has caused. Come on Lord, mud everywhere, on the clean and dirty clothes, splattered into corners that never see the light of day. Who will end up having to sort it all out?

Who ended up having to sort out mankind's mess? Stretch out your arms and embrace the absurdity of it all, but I love mankind. There is nothing more worthwhile than saving my creation, my children.

I am stumped now; my problems are nothing in comparison to what God has had to deal with over the centuries with his wayward people.

His love has never let us down. I say my 'Yes' again. My meditation is brought rapidly to an end as the hoover roars into action in the next room and promptly screams in agony as something is trapped in its jaws.

'Oh stupid thing.'

I jump up and investigate. Henry is trying to pull an item from the mouth of the hoover; he pulls so hard that there is a rip. I put my hand on his shoulder and take the machine in my hand, turn it over and unlock the plastic cover to reveal the insides. It is easier to untangle in this state and I present Henry with his, well I am not sure what his thing is. He goes bright red and takes it off me quickly.

'Is it an important item of clothing?' I ask.

He responds that it doesn't matter; it was a joke present and will be better off in the bin now it is ripped. He puts it in his pocket to hide his embarrassment and when I hand back the device he starts the chore again, not having learnt that it is a mistake to try and hoover over, under and around things. I decide to disappear downstairs as it is better for my blood pressure.

Oh Lord, trying though things are, there is always room for a lesson to be learnt.

Or is it? The hallway has Henry's football gear all over it, Gabby's left her wet towel on top of Bob's paperwork, and Lily Pink is trying to do a cartwheel in between the items. I look at the plaque that we have on the wall which says 'If you can survive this madhouse then you can survive the world!' and wonder if the world can survive us. The noise from the hoover stops and I figure out that Henry has done his best. He swings down the stairs as usual, hurriedly throws his kit into a bag, picks up Gabby's pink wet towel and stuffs it in on top.

He enquires how Johnny is, and suddenly I wonder too, then from the kitchen my son appears, all dressed in his uniform and ready to leave.

'I want to go to school,' he announces, as he passes me by, looking straight at Henry and telling him to hurry up.

101

'He's fine,' I say.

I am amazed at his strength of character, but then Johnny has surprised me already today.

'I'll keep an eye on him,' Henry whispers.

As they walk out the door, Johnny says that Gabby has already gone. She has done it again, sneaked off without a goodbye.

Oh Lord, my children are growing up; help me to allow them to do so. Things seem very different now; their needs are not so simple to identify apart from the hunger issues. Only LP is smaller; the others are as tall as or taller than me. They look down on me rather than the other way round. It is a strange feeling.

Sometimes I think this house is like a railway station with all the comings and goings. 'The train now arriving at platform 12 is the intercity non-stop express to Chaos. Change here for Refreshments, Ablutions and Sleep; next train will be departing in five minutes. If you experience disturbances while on your journey during, after or on the line do not panic, an engineer will be with you shortly, once the problem has been reported. There may be a delay due to shortage of staff, but remember you are important to us. Have a nice day.'

Bob disturbs my musings; he is looking for a tie. I pick one up from the banister and hand it to him and ask where Lily Pink is. He says she is eating her breakfast in the dining room. He pecks me on the cheek, picks up his wet papers, looks at them trying to figure out quite why they are in this state, and leaves for work. Lily Pink shoots out of the kitchen door and does another cartwheel. I am amazed that she is not sick and think that she must have a cast iron stomach.

Oh Lord, grant me serenity in these few moments before I have to start my own daily quest.

Lily Pink seems to be searching for something. When I enquire, she says that her blue shorts for PE are not where she put them. I have a sinking feeling that Henry probably stuck them in with all of his kit. I ask LP where she had left them.

'On the floor right here,' she comments looking bemused.

My suspicion appears to be correct. I suggest that we go and have a look for another pair. We find two in her drawer, one pair too large the other too small. She starts to panic and yells that she must have some shorts otherwise she will get detention. I think about that and wonder if ten year olds do actually get detention. I pull out a black pair, but it is discarded forcefully as it is the wrong colour. With a little persuasion I manage to get Lily Pink to at least put them in her bag and suggest that when she goes to put them on later she just says 'oops mum put the wrong ones in'. She looks at me wondering if I have a screw loose and raises her eyes to heaven. I say that that way it isn't her fault and she should get a more sympathetic response from the teacher. She is not convinced but it is the best I can do.

Oh Lord, what little trials our children have, I know that I am a trial to my children! That look of amazement when they were little when I said anything has gone. I am seen for who I am now, an adult who makes mistakes and is flawed. Father don't let me consent to feeling inferior. Give me the courage to be who I am.

Lily Pink is finally ready to set off for school, saying sorry for her actions. I appreciate her words and give her a hug before she leaves. Once again it is my turn to get ready and prepare for my morning at the preschool. I don my usual apparel, sweat shirt and jeans after a quick shower and then swallow a bowl of porridge and fruit. I put fun things into my bag, puppets, books, magic wand all to wow the little children and close the door on my personal life, well at least for the morning.

Oh Lord, sometimes it is hard to just shut the door and put on another hat. How many times do you do it each day? The Compassionate Hat, The Healer's Hat, The Teacher's Hat, and The Listening Ear Hat to name a few. It must look like a Tommy Cooper sketch, except you are perfect at making the changes, because you know our scripts personally. Help me to put the right hat on this morning.

As I push the door open to the preschool I hear laughter coming from the main room. It immediately puts a smile on my face and I walk in to see two of my colleagues grappling with putting away an instant ready tent. Apparently it had come out of its packaging and inflated itself to its ready state in the confines of the walk in cupboard where the toys are kept. There is a knack to folding it away and I can see that neither is acquainted with it. Instead, one of the ladies has a leg over one part trying to twist a pole that doesn't want to be twisted. Then the other helper is trying to push the piece she has into the bag while standing on another part to prevent it from popping up again. As soon as they see me they jump clear of the offending article and let it explode into its natural state while they collapse on the floor holding their stomachs in a fit of laughter. I put on my technical hat and in an instant I twist, curl, fight an awkward turn and then pack the tent into its tight fitting bag and tie the ends up. If only life could be that easy!

Oh Lord, did I hear you laugh? It must remind you of all the times I get myself twisted over some silly offending article that is in my path causing me confusion as I don't have instructions on how to deal with it. Laughable mistakes, what funny creatures we must be. Father help me to learn to laugh at the silliness of life's surprises which are brought about by my own creation.

An early arrival turns our attention from the fun and games. It is a new child hugging tightly to her mother's legs, looking overwhelmed by the vastness of the hall. She doesn't want to take off her coat nor look at the lovely toys. The little girl is completely bemused as to why her mother would want to leave her with strangers, whom she has met a couple of times, but in the security that mum was still in the room. Having been kissed goodbye and knowing that her mum is leaving very soon, she lets out a stream of screams that are high-pitched and tearless. Anger resonates the building. A Mickey Mouse hat appears.

'Look,' her mother says, 'you love Mickey Mouse!'

A short interval occurs, then the screaming resumes. My skilled colleague approaches with a mystery in her hand. It catches the little girl's attention. She slowly unwraps from her mother's leg to see what it is. Mum is encouraged to move quickly out of the room and to make her escape. The youngster is then led further into the room and sees and laughs as the secret is revealed to her. She does not look back but moves forward to a morning of enjoyment. How beautifully and professionally this encouragement is executed. I stand and celebrate my colleagues and their gifts.

Oh Lord, children are a joy to you. You have raised them up from being the lowest of the low by becoming a child yourself and exclaiming their true position in society as heirs to Your Kingdom. Father, may I always see you in their little faces.

Our preschool is wonderfully organised by the manager, her daybook ready with the jobs for us to do during the morning. Today I am a floater, meaning I can move among the different activities and help wherever I am needed. However I am also aware that I have some observations to do and to note the milestones achieved by the children I am responsible for. As I watch the flow of little people filling the rooms I am aware of their growing confidence and characters. Then a thought fills my mind. If I had been your key worker Lord, what would I write about you? 'Outgoing, confident, friendly, enjoys the company of both children and adults, initiates games, encourages and includes others, enjoys making things, has a great attention to detail, impressive language skills, loves stories and interactive creative play, is compassionate to those less able and seeks out those that are friendless, at snack time shares the food and checks that everyone has a drink, listens with interest as his peers converse with one another, is always polite and a joy to have in the mix. Little Jesus is also prone to wandering off and going about his Father's business'.

Oh Lord, all of these qualities are within a child when they are encouraged to emulate your likeness.

A hand is tugging at mine, blue eyes stare up at me and a hopeful face smiles and points to the climbing frame. She rushes off to the wooden equipment and waits for me to stand behind her, and then she attempts to climb the four rungs. Her little hands cling tightly as she pulls her weight upwards and then stops. Only just three, the petite girl stands still, not sure what to do next. Her leg won't stretch over the final rung. She is unable to look around at me as it will cause her to wobble, so I put my hands on the same rung and show her that she can with my help take one hand off and hold onto the plank just by her knees and crawl through the rungs. Monica decides that she would rather climb down with help than continue. I look at the child's disappointed face and decide that this is a case for the Mickey Mouse hat.

Oh Lord it is time to be a child again. To think of what will be acceptable and not condescending to a 3 year old. I thank you Father for giving me an inspirational thought.

We wander over to my bag of tricks and I put the hat on. Immediately Monica spots the scientific plastic tube with the water and stars in that move up and down as you turn it either way. I let her play with it for a bit and then suggest that we go over to the climbing frame again. As I am unable to shrink to the size of a three year old I get down on my hands and knees and pretend to ascend the play equipment. Monica is waving the plastic scientific wand thingy and pretending to magic me up the climbing frame. When I get to the rung that she had difficulty with I heave myself through the railings. Then it gets embarrassing as my bottom being very much larger than a three year olds, becomes stuck.

Oh Lord, this is embarrassing and wasn't part of the plan. I realise that I only half thought this out but I need a solution rather quickly if possible?

Monica is beside herself laughing thinking that this is purely for her enjoyment. One of my colleagues arrives on the scene and suggests that perhaps Monica ought to do a reverse wave of the wand thingy hoping that the climbing frame might release me of its clutches. Of course it works once I stop trying to push myself through and retrace my steps downwards. My hat is all bent and falling over my face but I manage to look dignified once all is restored to normal again. Having seen me in action Monica decides that she will not be beaten and asks me to wave the wand as she climbs. She carefully retraces her previous steps and before she gets to the fourth rung, flops onto the platform and crawls in without getting her bottom stuck! Her delight is obvious and her prize is to be able to slide down the semi-vertical plank of wood on the other side of the climbing frame. Once she has done this she looks at me quizzically.

'Why did your bottom get stuck Vicki?'

Good question. It is probably all those chocolates the manager keeps giving me!

Oh Lord, thank you for hearing my prayer and bringing someone to my aid. Thinking outside of the box can sometimes lead to precarious outcomes, but I am thankful that you have given me the ability to do so.

Monica thinks that I ought to do the climbing again; however I decide that once is enough, especially as it had the required outcome of Monica seeing that she can overcome a challenge when encouraged by an adult. Besides, I am not sure what Ofsted would make of my actions. They might have to write a whole new chapter on how to deal with professionals who use off-the-wall techniques.

Oh Lord, wasn't that one of your traits or was it that it just hadn't been seen before, because everyone was supposed to follow the book as it was written down. But your compassion went beyond the 'what the norm was' and you delivered what God wanted.

The Manager approaches me and she has two people with her. She introduces them and I start to sweat as the words Ofsted Inspectors swim around in my head. I still have my Mickey Mouse Hat on and I look around quickly to see if any little person needs a hand. Panic begins to well up into my throat and my speech becomes stuttered as I greet them both with a cockeyed smile and what feels like a twitch in my eye. JUGDEMENT DAY springs to mind. Did they see my contorted efforts on the climbing frame? Did I assess the implications of Health and Safety before I did my gung-ho bit? I can't think, stand still or stop the silly facial expressions that keep appearing on my face. Thankfully Monica saves me and leads me away to do some colouring with her, but I can't help thinking that during their stay they will want to talk and ask questions. I am hopeless at on-the-spot interrogations.

Oh Lord I am in panic mode, I feel that every move is being watched, written down and commented on. Help me to act naturally and to let my professionalism shine through.

At the colouring table there are four other children, all of varying abilities and ages. Danny asks me to draw a horse for him. I suggest a car might be easier but he insists on a horse as he needs one for his knight; they didn't have cars in those days, silly Vicki! A horse it is, but my attempts of drawing a horse are even worse than Danny's and he doesn't look impressed at my efforts.

'Vicki, why have you drawn a pond with an eye in it?' he enquires.

I try and encourage his imagination to see the shape of the horse but he just looks at me in disbelief. His friend Jordon offers to help out and I have to admit it is definitely an improvement on my effort.

Oh Lord of the imagination, how beautiful the world is to a three year old. They think of something to do and just do it, nothing is impossible to them. Whole worlds are conquered up in their minds, fantastical improvisation, and a trip to the moon, followed by an underwater exploration of a sunken ship. How awesome this imaginary world is. Help me to learn from these children that life is for living and dreaming the impossible.

Danny decides to cut the animal out and the next moment I hear a sobbing coming from his direction. I turn to him and realise that he has cut off the horse's legs. Well I imagine it is the legs, not being sure which way up it is. I put my arm around him and try to console his obvious disappointment. One of the Inspectors, who unbeknown to me is standing behind us, asks what the matter is. I inform her that Danny appears to have cut off his horse's legs when he interrupts with a sob saying that it wasn't the horse's legs but his head, and what was his knight going to do with a headless horse! Instead of diving in with a solution, mainly because I am not sure what it is, I wait for Danny to save the situation and pray that he comes up with a stunning suggestion.

Oh Lord and problem solver, you know what the answer is, that is why you chose twelve disciples to learn from you and to impart that knowledge to the rest of civilization. It is what we do with that knowledge that sets us apart from others and entices them to look beyond their own solutions for the true answer of Life.

Jordon looks very excited and tells Danny to sit next to him on the other side of the table.

'Look,' he says and Danny looks.

A wide smile breaks out on his tear stained face.

'Oh yes,' he exclaims, 'the horse looks better that way up, I can see a head and he can be a she instead.'

108

Both the Inspector and I jointly say out loud in unison, 'He's got an older brother or sister!' Neither of us can stop the muffled laughter. I feel a hand on my shoulder, we have broken the barrier.

Oh Lord, thank you that other people can show us a different perspective on a situation. How amazing that to one person a ruined piece of art can be seen as an alternative creation. Help me to see that my life is a work in progress and to look at the right side of the masterpiece instead of seeing all the knots that makes it up on the reverse side.

The new girl, Cara, joins us at the table; she decides to sit next to me and starts to eat a red crayon. I gently take the crayon and ask her to spit the contents out of her mouth into a tissue.

Cara then bursts into tears. 'I want my mummy.'

I gently tell her that mummy will be back to collect her at the end of the morning and that she will be so proud of Cara for being such a good girl at preschool. With Danny and Jordon playing with their art pieces I suggest that Cara and I go and have a little look at my special bag. I take off my Mickey Mouse hat and put on a Goofy one instead. My speech instantly changes to the cartoon character's voice and my body sways backwards and forwards, in a relaxed over-the-top impression, of a dog standing on his hind legs trying not to fall over.

Oh Lord, I know you can see me now, I hope you are laughing because you gave me this funny sense of humour.

Goofy is of course one of Mickey's best friends and being a bit educationally challenged is perfect for an eccentric like me to copy.

'Gawrsh, are you new today too?' Cara nods. 'Do you tink you could be my fwend and pray with me?

She takes my hand, wipes the tear away from her cheek onto her sleeve and then shows me all the different play stations. By the time we have seen everything Cara is very animated when we sit down by the doll's house.

109

'Are you feeling better now Goofy?' she enquires.

In character I say 'Yes, much better, specially as I have a fwend now.' She gives Goofy a hug and I know she will be okay.

Oh Lord, you love befriending your people. Everyone is worth going that extra mile for in your eyes. Help me to follow your lead and open my arms to all who need comfort.

The children are all called to gather around Becky our manager. She explains that everyone needs to go to the toilet and wash their hands before sitting down for their snack. They all file into a long line, older children helping the younger ones as they walk to the toilets. I meanwhile head for the kitchen to prepare the snack and drinks. Twenty eight cups and plastic plates are stacked up on the trolley. I chop up apples and carrots and place them on five plates along with some grapes. Then pour milk into five jugs and make-up three cups of orange juice for those children that don't have milk. All is prepared.

Oh Lord, you fed your people when you saw that they were hungry. Your food was from heaven for the mind, heart and soul but you did not neglect the physical hunger either that was present when you were meeting with the crowds. Father I hunger for your words with my mind, heart and soul. Quench my thirst, satisfy my need for you.

The children having toileted, washed their hands and filed into the snack area, sit at the tables and say the preschool 'thank you' prayer for what they are about to eat. I pass the snacks through the hatch and the young people munch and drink happily. I have prepared some toast too as these little explorers need something to sustain their energy levels for the outdoor-play that is next. All finished they go and put on their coats and emerge into the outside world of fresh air. For me it is the washing up. I watch and smile through the window as I see the antics of some of the children who have turned the old car tyres into boats and are pirates on the high seas. The mountain of cups and plates are soon washed and dried. The tables are cleaned and put away along with the chairs.

Oh Lord, there is so much we don't see of your activities behind the scenes that go on in everyday life, little pieces in the jigsaw puzzle that needs to be placed before we

110

move onto the next sequence of events. Father how awesome it is to know that You are right now concerned with every minute detail of my life, no matter how small or great the puzzle piece is that needs to be fitted together, in order to create the complete picture for this moment in time.

Little red faces appear in the main room en route to the clothes pegs. Coats are hung up with the help of an adult and then a calming routine is engaged upon. The children are asked to lie down and close their eyes. Some find this hard to do and peek out of one eye. There is a giggle here and a wriggle there. Some lie on their backs, some on their fronts, some with bottoms in the air and others curled up into a ball. All have their own special position.

Oh Lord, do you have a lump in your throat when you see a picture like this? Total trust. Such a beautiful tableau.

The two inspectors are sitting in the Art room talking to the Manager and her deputy. I am signalled to go and join them. Both the members of the senior management team leave with one of the inspectors and I am left alone with the other. She smiles and I return the favour. She asks me if I like working at the preschool to which I answer enthusiastically in the positive. Then the more specific questions start relating to the curriculum, the stepping stones of age related activities, the challenging of minds and bodies, the encouragement and understanding of special needs, health and safety and the final exploration of my mental wellbeing.

'How many hats do you possess?'

'Probably too many,' I respond.

The inspector seems to be happy with my answers.

'I can see all the staff are dedicated to the children; however there is one concern I have. I really think you ought to have a Minnie Mouse hat as I would have liked to have seen her make an appearance.' I ask if she is going to include that in her official report.

Oh Lord, questions and verdicts, how our lives can depend on them. Are we performing correctly according to the ideals and strict regulations of an official body?

111

How you know about that. At least if I fail the worst will be the loss of a job, for you it was the loss of your life.

I am the last to be seen by the officials today and know that some of my colleagues will be entertaining them tomorrow. When I leave the Art room I am aware that the story is being read to the children. It is nearly home time. I am grateful that I have now been through the microscopic observances and pray that all our efforts have been recognised as beneficial to the children and our colleagues. All of a sudden I feel extremely tired and just want to say goodbye to the morning and all its stress. Fortunately the preschool does not need too much tidying up after the session, and after a prayer for us, and for the inspectors, we all make our own way home for lunch.

Oh Lord, thank you for this morning, for the sudden arrival of the two ladies whose job it is to ensure good practice is observed by preschool professionals. I know they are doing their job and it is only by questioning and observation that this can be done. Father, may their judgement be fair by their standards, but in all things I know that you are the ultimate Judge to whom I must be obedient.

Vicki, you have given unto Caesar what is Caesar's and to God what is God's. Thank you.

Afternoon Prayer

Lunch is quick, a sandwich and a cup of tea as I have to go quickly to do the food shopping. The supermarket is only a few miles away and with trolley in tow I start my big shop. Vegetables, meat, cheese, milk, bread the usual sustenance, as well as some fattening produce that teenagers woof down to keep hunger at bay. As I am looking at the drinks I hear a commotion coming from the baking aisle. I feel uneasy about the shouting.

Strike one

I leave my trolley and look around the next aisle and there in front of me is an angry lady. She is humiliating her child with her words.

Strike two

Then she smacks him.

Strike three

She walks off and leaves him crying.

Strike four

The lady returns looming over her son and tells him he is a despicable child not worthy of any attention or food.

Strike five

She commands him to stand where he is as she doesn't want to see or hear from him.

Strike six

He pleads for forgiveness and his mother refuses it.

Strike seven

The little boy stretches out his arms for comfort and she turns her back.

Strike eight

I can no longer bear the boys distress and step carefully up to him and ask if he is okay, of course he isn't but it is a safe thing to say, he looks at me with woeful eyes. His mother storms back and lashes out at me verbally for interfering.

Strike nine

I try to negotiate a truce with her for her son's sake, but enraged by my unwanted concern she pushes me forcefully with her hands and I fall against the racking.

Strike ten

The lady laughs, looks at the boy and yells at him saying, 'Look what you have done with your snivelling,' and hits him around the face.

Strike eleven

The boy cowers and his mother tells him to stop whimpering and to be a man.

Strike twelve

As the woman takes her son unceremoniously by the wrist his eyes catch mine and I look with sympathy as he walks away knowing that there may well be worse to come for this little lad when he gets home. I say to him, 'It's not your fault,' so that only he can hear me.

Oh Lord, You know, You were there, You love her even though she is guilty of this sin, and You died for her as well as for the little boy. I am lost for words.

One of the store assistants comes and gives me a hand to get up. I am shaken but more disturbed about what I have witnessed concerning the boy. People heard the commotion but no one except me saw what had happened. The manager is sent for, but by the time he arrives and we have combed the store and checkout area the woman and the boy are nowhere to be seen. I know that the boy will have to take his chances and I pray for his protection and for the temper of his mother. God help them both.

Oh Lord, I feel angry and defenceless. A child has been abused by an adult, by someone who ought to know better. I do not know what will happen to him and that is what disturbs me most. A lamb led to the slaughter.

The Manager asks if I want him to call the police and make a statement about what happened. I decide that this might be a good idea. I report the incident to the constable on his arrival and give a description of the woman and her child. The policeman seems aware of this family and says he will look into the matter. He asks if I want to press charges to which I answer no as I only want to protect the little boy. He says that he might need to question me again at a later stage and takes down my details in his notebook. The ordeal over I return to my trolley, it is still parked in the same place as I had left it. I feel a bit sick and shaky, so I do the rest of the shopping as best I can, pay for it and leave the supermarket.

Oh Lord, whatever we do to the least of us we do to you, no one deserves to be humiliated in public. Not a king, nor a child.

Time is now getting on and I need to be back home for Lily Pink's arrival. On the drive home I begin to feel the after effects of my experience. Tears start to well up and flow down my face. The hopelessness in the eyes of the little boy, as though he knew he was of no consequence. His plea for forgiveness snubbed. The coldness of his persecutor. The policeman recognising the description of the assailant, showed that this was not the first time she had been reported. Her judgement that compassion is a weakness and needs to be brushed away and crushed. As I pull into our driveway I see Lily Pink standing by the front door. I quickly get out of the car and hug her; she looks up at me, sees the tears and asks what is wrong.

'I love you Lily Pink so very much.' It is all I can manage.

She replies, 'I know mum and I love you too.'

Oh Lord, thank you that you love me.

Lily Pink helps me bring in the shopping and we both put the groceries away. LP carefully watches me like a mother hen to see if I am going to cry again, I am done with the tears and am grateful for the life I have which is challenging but safe. I need a cup of tea. The warming answer to all my stresses, apart from a hot bath with a good book. With tea in hand I walk into the sitting room to see Lily Pink enthroned in front of the television watching a children's spy series. During the advert she jumps up and pretends to be a ninja. I smile and chuckle at her antics, how lovely to see her freedom of expression.

Oh Lord, up lifter of all that were and are downtrodden, God who became man through Jesus, Comforter in our world, passionate lover. I lift up all those that are not as fortunate as my daughter, who are not allowed or able to express themselves freely, I am sorry if I have given cause for any of my family to feel dispirited or unloved. Give me a renewed desire to encourage and facilitate your gifts in my family for your honour and glory.

Suddenly there is a crash. The noise resonates from the living room, then silence. I am aware that the other three from my clan should be arriving almost immediately. I am wondering if I ought to see what caused the noise and to make sure Lily Pink is alright. But before I can react at all the front door opens and my brood are disarming themselves of school bags, coats, shoes, art folder and PE kit, building an obstacle course in their wake. Gabby opens the door to the living room, says 'Hi' to Lily Pink and then just stands there.

'You could give me a hand you know,' Lily Pink pleads to which Gabby, Henry and Johnny file in and start to detangle her from the clothes drier. It's one of those moments that you have to get a photograph of for the album, as no one would believe the image otherwise. Lily Pink is protesting against having the evidence publicised but isn't in much of a position to do anything about it.

Oh Lord, a picture speaks a thousand words, this is attributed to an early Emperor of the Xia Dynasty in China about 4,000 years ago, but your masterpiece from the moment of creation is testimony that it should have been cited as your saying. Your album of our life must be enormous, as you know everything about us. You delight in every good thing we do, and you forgive every thought and action that is not of you. Thank you Father that I am a picture that speaks a thousand words and that I am in your treasured album.

As Lily Pink is released from the jaws of the clothes drier my imagination starts to take over. What if Jesus' parents had had a camera? What pictures would they have taken? Probably the same as everyone else. I turn the imaginary pages of the photo album: Mary points, Jesus in the womb; Baby Jesus just born; Baby Jesus smiling for the first time; Baby Jesus' first bed; Baby Jesus' first friend; The happy parents with Jesus; Jesus' first tooth; Jesus crawling for the first time; Jesus walking; Jesus holding a chisel; Jesus with his first cut/graze; Jesus' first haircut; thousands of photographs, taken with the eye, never published or seen. Thousands of portraits have been painted since from the imagination and inspiration from artists all over the world. Each has tried to depict Jesus' nature, but who really knew what Jesus looked like, do I?

Oh Lord of mystery, reveal yourself to me. Become as clear as a picture to my heart so that I can mirror your glory through my eyes and bring you to those that do not know you as their Lord and maker.

Vicki, look no further, you were created in my image and likeness.

I am brought back suddenly from my wanderings as the four pass by me heading upwards to their rooms.

'When will dinner be? I am starving,' Henry says.

Henry then turns on his heels in front of everyone as he decides to descend the stairs, causing chaos in the confined space. He stands next to me, but seems to want to go into the kitchen for a more private chat. He sits on the stool and folds his arms. I look at him with a questioning expression.

117

'She said yes.'

'Who?' I utter, not quite comprehending the shortness of the conversation, and then a light bulb appears. 'Oh, the girl you wanted to ask out?'

'Yes,' he said again.

I suggest that that is a good thing.

He looks down at his knees, 'Guess so,' he agrees.

I can see that he is still uncomfortable about the situation. I ask when he is going to take her out and he shrugs a 'not sure'. I intimate that a simple date might be acceptable first, for instance a meeting at a coffee shop to get to know one another better and then maybe a game of bowls if the talking gets awkward? He breaths out a sigh of relief and I can see that it meets with his approval, he starts to get off the stool and I change the subject to Johnny.

Oh Lord and matchmaker, who said that finding your soul mate was easy. Girls are an enigma to boys and vice versa. Father you have had the longest courtship with your people and still we don't understand the depths of your Love. Am I ready for the Wedding day when we finally see one another face to face?

Henry states that Johnny has had a reasonable day; the teachers were looking out for him and making sure that there were no repercussions from yesterday. The Chaplain had seen Johnny at lunch time and then spoken with Henry afterwards. Mr Moore had been encouraged by Johnny making the decision to come to school after yesterday, and felt that this courage would help him move forward. He would pray that Johnny would be able to forgive the students who had made his life miserable. Henry looked at me and said that he wasn't sure that he agreed with this sentiment. I reassure Henry that things happen for a reason and as usual we can't see the full knock-on effect that this episode will have. I know he hates injustice and I recognise his frustration. It is not nice to feel helpless and leave things in the hands of others to deal out the punishment. I hug him and he asks, 'What's for tea?'

Oh Lord, and powerful forgiver, help me to understand that forgiveness comes from Heaven, it is not man made. The world changed because Forgiveness lived amongst us. Forgiveness came into a world where punishing your enemies was expected and seen as a great trophy. I cannot move forward to the next stage if I do not forgive. Jesus, You knew that, understood that and moved on to the next stage: Arrest, Cross, Resurrection. Your yes to forgiveness allowed the course of history to change forever. I cannot forgive on my own, it takes Your Spirit alive in me to help me make that decision and follow it through. Please give me the courage to do that.

Tea, yes what is for tea? Sausage pie I think, home-made, bit of sausage meat, onions, chopped tomatoes, seasoning, flour, egg, all encased in puffed pastry with some salad. With the recipe in the oven, the phone rings. I ponder whether to pick it up or just leave it, and by the time I decide it rings off. Then it goes again. I figure that it must be important for it to ring a second time. As I am about to pick up the receiver it stops. I return to the kitchen and it starts again. This time I hurl myself full force towards the instrument and declare who I am and ask who is speaking, there is a click and then the purr. Then a smell of burning, burning! With an Olympic hop, skip and jump I land in the kitchen literally and bang my head on the breakfast bar. Dizzy I stand up and pull the frying pan off the energy source. A few stranded crisp onions are sizzling, having avoided being put into the sausage pie. However the main burning smell is actually from a drop of oil under the frying pan causing a strand of smoke to wind its way up into the atmosphere.

Oh Lord and master chef, how I wish I had your talent of feeding the five thousand with very little interruption.

I call the foursome and they bear down hungrily on the sausage pie and salad, asking for seconds. The telephone rings again. Gabby answers it with a mouth full of food, 'E us usy a e moemp.' She swallows her masticated sausage mix and tells me it is granddad. I take the phone.

'Is that you Vicki?' he asks.

I reply, 'Yes,' and ask him if everything is alright.

'It's your mum, I can't find her anywhere. Have you seen her?'

At that moment I can hear my mother trying to take the telephone off my father. 'Let me speak to Vicki.'

'Get off you old hag. What have you done with my wife?'

A real tussle ensues and finally my mum hastily tells me not to worry, everything is alright, dad is just having one of his moments and the phone is disconnected.

Oh Lord, I cannot help my mother with my father at present but I offer up this prayer as a gift of my love. Father be with them now and bring strength and patience into their situation. Calm my father's anguished mind and bring him peace.

By the time I get to the sausage pie it is all gone so I do myself a salad sandwich and pop a slice of cheese in. Lily Pink does not want me to do my usual Thursday night studying as she has homework to do and wants my help. I remind her that her dad helps her on a Thursday so that I can have some time to do my college work. She looks at me with very big eyes, but I refuse to allow them to weaken me into giving up my evening.

Oh Lord, you took time out, how enticing the mountains must have seemed when the crowds flocked around you and gave you little peace from their needs. As much as you loved your people even you needed space. Father, help me to honour my needs.

Before I go and start my essay on 'The role of Women in the Twenty First Century', I knock on Johnny's door. He tells me it is open so I go in and ask if I can sit on his bed. He moves his legs out of the way so that there is room for me. He looks at me and says, 'Hi,' an indication that he is okay about having a conversation. I keep it short and ask if his day has been alright. He nods and says, 'Not bad.' Nobody had bugged him but then nobody had spoken to him either. His best friend had taken the day off. I tell him then that he is very brave and I am extremely proud of him. He shrugs and says an embarrassed thanks. I ask Johnny about his left hand and he shows it to me. It is looking amazing, very little redness and hardly any sign that he had suffered a burn there. Then he breaks out into an excited rambling about how his maths and science teachers want him to take his GCSE's early as he is so clever and are sure he will pass them without any problems.

120

'They said I was gifted and talented,' and so you are I thought. His eyes were full of excitement, something I see so rarely in this young man. I compliment him on his achievement, especially as it has been down to his own enthusiasm and hard work.

Oh Lord, thank you that my son has been given a light for his road ahead. Thank you that the teachers decided to tell him today this news, so that he would think forward instead of dwell on the pain of yesterday. Father, my life is cluttered with yesterdays; help me to look forward instead of backwards. Help me to be excited about my future.

As I sit at my little desk in the bedroom and look at the blank page underneath the heading, Bob enters the room and enquires as to what I am doing. I remind him that tonight is Thursday, my evening for doing course work, and his evening of being homework monitor. His face says it all. But then I tell him Johnny's great news and his mood lifts, he puffs out his chest.

'I knew he was special, what fabulous news, he's going to make it, isn't he?'

I take Bob's face into my hands and say, 'Yes he is,' and we kiss tenderly knowing that the years of worry and concern about his future will now be brighter, not easy, but certainly more hopeful with this news.

Oh Lord, we worry, we care, and we react as we need to, to all the ups and downs of life, in very human ways. As my Saviour I know that all is for a purpose, but still I worry and respond to that worry in my frail way. Father, embolden me to be strong, help me to listen to Your word and believe in your solutions, so that my weakness can become your strength.

Vicki, have I ever failed you?

Evening Prayer

'The role of Women in the Twenty First Century.' I think about the topic and realise that there is a lot that can be written about this subject, maybe that is why it is chosen as an essay for my English 'A' level, which I am studying via the medium of distance learning. Women have many roles, like my hats at preschool; they are constantly juggling them each day of their life according to what role is needed at any moment. I open my bible for inspiration and find Proverbs 14 verse 1 staring at me. "A wise woman builds her home, but a foolish woman tears it down with her own hands". It appears to me that we are all possibly foolish as we are driven endlessly with tasks to do; career (full or part time), homemaker, mother and wife to name a few and each role requires time and effort. How do we build up our home when we are so busy? In doing the building do we end up tearing it down out of frustration because we can't be everything to everyone? Are we setting up an impossible task for ourselves? Have we lost sight of what is important because of high mortgage costs, the cost of living, the expense of children and their needs as well as my needs and my husband's? All these pressures can lead to tearing the house down. So am I a wise woman in the Twenty First Century? If this was a subject on my school report I expect I might get an 'in need of improvement' or 'could try harder'.

Oh Lord, life just seems to be packed with so much, our house full to the brim of things yet to do. Help me Father to build up a safe, happy, caring, encouraging and peaceful home, where efforts are rewarded and tolerance is given to those things that have yet to be accomplished.

I attempt to type something on the computer.

'Don't call me an idiot!' resounds from the other side of the door.

'Just because I forgot to put the top on the shampoo.'

The girls are arguing at the top of their voices. One can't wash her hair because the shampoo has dribbled away during the day having fallen upside down into the bath, and the other because her sister is using her special towel. I thought they were supposed to be doing their homework! Dare I say anything? I think not!

Oh Lord, knowing when to intervene in any situation is an art. Father of this moment, silence the arguing.

I put my fingers in my ears to try and deaden some of the noise, however I can't type if I do this, so I put my earphones in and turn on the music on my MP3 player. The first song almost makes my eyes pop out as it is on full volume. I scramble to turn it down, probably taking the phones out of my ears would have been a better option, but I am in startle mode and not thinking straight.

Oh Lord, You are in the whisper of the air, the trickle of the stream, the drop of a snow flake, as well as in the booming noise of a rock star. Praise you God for the ringing in my ears.

The song is called Perfect by Pink, I really like the lyrics but not quite that loud. I have made a wrong turn more than once in my life, and certainly bad decisions on more than one occasion, so yes welcome to my silly life and back to my essay! The point is do I want to be a woman of the twenty first century? Stressed, put upon by employers who want the earth from you, and when they have taken it, spit you out without a bye-your-leave. Knowing all my rights and my children's rights, having the option to sue at every corner if things are not going my way. Having the latest of everything from designer babies to cosmetic face lifts. Paying to put off the inevitable. Why can't I be me? The model I was based on has survived from the beginning of time. It is perfect because it was made in the image and likeness of God. Is the woman of the twenty first century modelling your image or just hiding behind a façade? What is it that we are so frightened of?

Oh Lord, you did not come to change us but to free us from ourselves, to bring hope to our sinful nature. Father help me to stay true to Your calling, help me not to get bogged down by worldly desires but to contemplate your Glory.

At last I feel I have some direction for my essay. The words flow onto my laptop and I can feel the power of my thoughts being expressed. When I get an inspiring idea writing is not difficult for me. I love the images it conjures up and I have always felt that I am a story teller in the making. Maybe that is why I love the Bible so much as it is full of stories of the weak becoming strong, of God choosing the undesirable, society's cast-offs, and the least likely as his messengers. How would that sit with our media and advertisers today? Can you imagine a wild looking half-starved man called John the Baptist saying 'Spring Fresh, the natural water that cleans you from the inside out!' How many people would be instantly drawn? John would have to be air brushed and spring cleaned, a six pack superimposed onto his body, to look like a reasonable exponent of spring water and its healing qualities, otherwise it might advertise that if you drink this water you might look and behave half crazed afterwards. Not that John the Baptist was. Anyway I know what I mean.

Oh Lord and artistic designer, how natural is your world, unblemished by artificial accessories. When I see the sun shining or the stars glistening I know the purity of their maker. Help me to see through unblemished eyes the natural beauty of each and every one of your children and the amazing purity of their soul.

My mind starts to wander and I think of other adverts that I have seen that have annoyed me because of their idea that we should look amazing after a day's work and catering for our families and ready for a night of lust with our husbands, partners or whoever else we fancy jumping into bed with. These models who flounce around with bouncy hair that stays in place all day, whose make up looks as perfect as when they put it on in the morning and have gorgeous legs up to their armpits and have given birth to two children and can wear a bikini that shows no stretch marks. Who are the advertisers kidding? I look like I have thrown my make-up on, cried it all off, brushed the mascara all over my face, have a hole in my tights, brushed my hair while walking backwards through a bush, am challenged in height, have a stomach that droops earthward, boobs that are competing with my stomach and feet that are so small that they barely hold me upright. There is no way I can ever look like these visions and to be honest I am not sure that I want to. The role of Women in the Twenty First Century, well, perhaps it should be to stand up for who we really are?

Oh Lord, I can no longer be a six foot tall blonde beauty than I can a tightrope walker. Please help me to be happy with who I am and with the gifts and challenges that you have given me.

The essay written I save it and open Skype to see if anyone is on line. Bob is the only one. I am pleased that I have finished it and realise that time has flown. The house is strangely quiet. The icon flashes in the right hand corner on the computer and it shows that I have a message on Skype. Bob is asking how I am doing with my essay. I reply and ask him if he knows where everyone is? He imagines that they are in their bedrooms as they have finished their homework. I even think that they might have gone to bed as I am sure it is at least Lily Pink's bedtime. I ponder on whether I ought to go and see my daughters and decide that no noise is good, at least I hope it is and venture downstairs to watch my favourite TV show. I identify with the comic and love her take on life. I manage to see the whole episode with no interruptions, a rare treat indeed.

Oh Lord, I love to laugh and to be entertained by those that make me laugh. Thank you for those that have the talent to make us smile at our lives and see the funny side of things.

Having exercised my lungs and checked that my tear ducts are working through the medium of laughing, I feel it is time for a cup of tea. As I walk out of the living room I can hear some whispering on the dog leg staircase.

'Tell her, Gabby.'

'No she will be really cross.'

Ignoring the whispering I walk into the kitchen. I feel that it is better to wait until Gabby is ready to reveal whatever it is that will make me cross. From the corner of my eye I see my eldest daughter standing in the Kitchen doorway with a towel around her head. She bursts into tears so I just move towards her and enfold her in my arms. No matter what it is we can handle it. Gabby attempts to move away from me so I unwind my arms and she takes off her towel. Wow, pink hair!

Oh Lord, I wasn't expecting that!

I am not quite sure what to say. In some ways it looks very fetching; it brings out Gabby's rosy red cheeks. On another level it is quite funny, but I can see that my daughter doesn't think so, so I decide that it is better not mentioning that fact.

'I didn't know we had pink hair colouring in the bathroom!' is all I can think of saying.

Bob decides to walk into the Kitchen at this point and bluntly with a loud voice states the obvious.

'What have you done to your hair, it's pink? You have school tomorrow, what were you thinking of. You can't go to school like that madam.'

Gabby turns and runs, heading for the front door. She doesn't seem bothered that she has her pyjamas on. She just needs to get away from the obvious statement made by Bob.

'Will it come out?' My husband asks me. I say something about jumping in with big feet and he looks at me confused.

Oh Lord, we all make mistakes; although I am not sure I have made a pink one! Help me to sort this one out, or if this is not possible, then a friend who has knowledge of dealing with dyeing mistakes might be helpful.

I catch up with Gabby and apologise for her dad's comments and state that it was a bit of a surprise for him and that is why he reacted as he did. She stays silent for a short while as we turn around and head back home. Meanwhile I am racking my brains trying to think of a solution. But I need not worry as Gabby has a flash of inspiration. She literally runs the last paces to the front door, legs it up the stairs and closes her bedroom door. Lily Pink looks at me for an explanation and I just shrug my shoulders as I don't have one. I suggest that she gets herself off to bed. L P comments that dad hasn't told her to do so yet. I give her 'the look' and she hot foots it upstairs. Five minutes later Gabby is asking me for a lift to her friend's house. She has the bottle of hair colouring in her hand.

Oh Lord, when you created us we were carte blanche, but there were factors in our genes that decided what colour hair and eyes we inherited. So often we are not happy with what we have been given, and decide to change these things and mistakes happen in our experimentation. Thank you Father that we are not mistakes in your eyes.

I enquire where we are going and she gives me the address. I look at my watch and it is already ten o'clock. I am glad that her friend lives only a couple of miles away, but still it is a bit late for major hair surgery. We are welcomed by a young fashionable mum whose hair is almost the same colour as Gabby's apart from the fact that it has purple and blue in it as well.

'I thought you were doing it at the weekend love?' She comments.

Gabby then tells the lady that she hadn't meant to. She mistook it for her usual shampoo. Without further ado, Gabby is swept in and taken to the bathroom and I am left to wait downstairs. Whatever was used to remove the dye worked fairly well. On inspection I can only see a few hints of pink, and they are toned down. With a lot of reassurance by the multi-coloured hair lady, Gabby accepts that her hair has been restored to a reasonable semblance of normality. I thank the woman and apologise for the emergency and late hour. She just smiles and winks at Gabby.

'We girls must stick together.'

I don't like secrets and I feel like I am being left out of a conversation here.

Oh Lord, we grow, we fall, we win, we lose, we struggle, we cope, we laugh, we cry, we make our way through life. You watch, you listen, you lead, you stand back, you encourage, you heal, you care, and you teach us the path we should follow, so many lessons and only one life. Help me Father to take those opportunities which are often presented as problems and use them to enrich my life's experience.

In the car home I ask Gabby what the lady meant by 'you were supposed to be doing your hair at the weekend and girls sticking together?' Gabby looks out of the window, not wanting to look at me. It seems that she would rather not answer my question. With only a few minutes to go before we arrive home my daughter replies.

127

'She understands me; she thinks you are a bit behind the times and that you ought to let me express myself. That's why she gave my friend the pink hair dye to give to me to try. She said if I have any problems with you over it I could call her and she would talk to you.'

As soon as we stop in the drive way Gabby gets out of the car without letting me respond to her proclamation.

Oh Lord and mediator, have I missed something here? I have always tried to be open to my children's ideas and needs, so what has happened for my daughter to be in cahoots with someone else like this? Father walk ahead of me and open the door so that I can communicate with Gabby to find out what has happened.

Bob greets me at the door and asks if all is alright now. I nod as Gabby quickly passes my husband in the doorway. She says goodnight and disappears. He says that Cathy rang earlier asking if I was still going round to see her and he said that it was very unlikely as I was dealing with a very pink problem. Cathy hadn't found it a very convincing excuse and hoped I would explain myself tomorrow if I managed to break free of my family obligations in order to give her a few moments of my precious time. We go inside and he makes me that cup of tea that I didn't have earlier. I confide in Bob about what was said in the car and he concludes that we leave it for now as it is late and wait for Gabby to open up about this event when she is ready. I feel that Bob is right, now is not the right time. He gives me a hug and I rest in his wonderful arms, feeling the power of his strength. I suddenly feel exhausted and all I want is to go to bed and sleep. Bob tells me to retire and that he will bring up the tea when it is ready.

Oh Lord, sometimes all we need is a hug, nothing more. Thank you for the hugs I have received throughout my life. Thank you for your hugs Father.

Vicki, my arms are always open to you.

Night Prayer

I have a quick shower and climb into bed, glad that the day is almost over. But before I close my eyes I know that I must just reflect on my day and offer it up to my Father in Heaven.

Oh Lord, I am so tired. As usual the day has bought many challenges and issues. I lift up my day to you and pray that your will has been done through me in my thoughts and deeds. I hope that my 'yes' was acceptable in your sight.

Vicki, you have been very brave today. Your 'yes' was acceptable as I was scourged in the supermarket. Each lash tore at my flesh, each word crushed my spirit but your gaze made the pain bearable and your presence gave me strength.

I remember the boy and his mother. But I didn't stop the actions.

My dear one you couldn't stop the actions, the assailant was a bully, she had no intentions of stopping. But you noticed, you made your presence known and you showed the boy that he counted as somebody worth speaking up for. He will not forget you, nor will I.

But I wanted to do more. He was only a child, unable to defend himself.

Be comforted by the fact you did everything you could. Thank you.

I think about these words and wonder if I always do my best. With so many balls in the air to juggle at any one time, is it possible to do our best? I think that perhaps it is if our hearts are honourable to the moment in hand.

Oh Lord, Your sacrifice was honourable; you did not hype it up or do it out of pride to show what you can do for mankind. You didn't look for Superstar status; you spoke your message, acted upon it, and consequently suffered and died for it. You did the best you could in an understated way. Father help me to mirror your best.

Vicki, each day you say 'yes' to me you are giving me your best, I know the answer in that response is from a willing soul. As you sleep my spirit will renew, strengthen and heal your body, mind and soul so that tomorrow we can continue our Holy Week. Be blessed Victoria Sponge.

Chapter Five

Friday

Morning Prayer

'Humble yourselves, therefore, under God's mighty hand, that he may lift you up in due time. Cast all your anxiety on him because he cares for you. Be alert and of sober mind. Your enemy the devil prowls around like a roaring lion looking for someone to devour.' - Simon Peter; 1 Peter 5:6-8 (New International Version)

I can hear Bob snoring next to me, he looks so peaceful, but the lines of life are beginning to tell on his face. We were in our early twenties when we met and I knew straight away that I wanted to spend the rest of my life with him, growing together and raising our children. He was that quiet man who sat on his own in church, and left without saying hello or goodbye to anyone. He just appeared and disappeared each Sunday. Slowly I managed to make eye contact with him and in time he smiled back at me. Then I took courage in hand and sat next to him and introduced myself. Each Sunday became a day of longing, longing to know my Father better and for knowing this gentle man. Finally Bob asked me out. We went for walks and generally enjoyed one another's company, not worrying if we lapsed into times of silence, and often there were a lot. Bob being an only child had got used to his own company and conversation could be hard for him. But we had something in common, Parachutes. As the American Poet, William Stafford stated *'I have woven a parachute out of everything broken.'* And that is what we had both done. We flew separately until we met each other and allowed God to take our brokenness and weave a pattern of hope in between each coloured fragment that made our parachutes. The day we married (ten years after we had first met) we knew our parachutes would take us up into storms of cloud as well as to the calm waters as we journeyed together. But we knew that with the mighty hand of God watching over us we could ride through the complexities of life and hold on to the hope that sealed us together.

Oh Lord, each day I say 'yes' to you I also say yes to my husband, my children and my life whatever it may hold. Father, almighty and powerful, enormous in your giving and love, thank you that I mean so much to you. This is such an incredible thought, to know that I am loved by You, the most awesome God who created all things, whose tiniest detail mattered, who left nothing unturned, nothing blank. I stagger at your talent, overcome by your intricate designs. And to think that this is only a fraction of what Heaven is like. How could I look at your creation and not believe. And yet I know that my faith is fragile and without it I would fall and become blind to you. Thank you Father for giving me the gift of faith, may I never cast it aside or refuse to believe in its significance in this world and my life.

The alarm goes off; morning has arrived in the household. I shoot up out of bed and rush into the bathroom first. Put the shower on and stand relaxing as the water gushes over my head and body. Then there is a banging on the door, and my 'me' time is over in the shower. I grab a dry towel, throw it over myself and put another one over my head and unlock the door. Not being able to see I do not know who has interrupted my moment of refreshment. Dripping I collide into another body, and I hear a little person say.

'I hate Fridays.'

'I thought it was Mondays that most people don't like.'

The voice concluded that Fridays were worse because the day was full of Maths and English and boring stuff.

Oh Lord, how easy it is to wish our days away when they are structured in such a way that we have no control over them. Day turns to night so quickly and yet we moan about what fills it. Father, help me to bless each day and to be grateful for the moments that makes up each day.

I can't find any underwear in my chest of drawers which means they are in a pile waiting to be put away. Still with my towel on I make my way downstairs to the utility room. The bowl with the clean washing in is upturned and the cat is sitting on some of the clothes. I search through the pile under the cat and put my hand on something unpleasant. I withdraw it quickly and the smell indicates that it is a present from my furry friend; she must have been sick on top of the clothes and then knocked over the basket as she jumped off. Cleaning up cat sick is not one of my favourite jobs, and with the notion that I have to rummage through the clean clothes and find what has been regurgitated on just turns my stomach.

Oh Lord, all I wanted was a pair of pants!

As I bend down my towel falls off revealing my naked body, and as I am about to check the clothing I remember the sick on my hand. I wipe it off on the towel. It is too cold to stand around in the nude so I put the towel back on thinking that I had turned it around the other way to avoid the sticky mess I had just put on it. Wrong. It is now on my chest, and the smell is wafting up into my nostrils. It doesn't take long for a reaction from my stomach. I hot foot it to the downstairs toilet and find it locked, I can't speak without fear that a gush of vomit will explode from my mouth. I don't make it in time to the cupboard under the kitchen sink with the bucket in and the floor receives the full force of my delivery.

Oh Lord, I know that a crisis is another word for an opportunity, but I am not sure I really wanted to wash my kitchen floor this early in the morning!

A voice sounds in alarm from behind me.

'Uh, you've got nothing on mum,' Henry exclaims.

I ask him to get me a towel and he spots the one in the utility room. He asks why there is vomit all over the place and he carefully steps around the splashes of sick and places it over my back. Then he comments that it has something horrible on it! Great! I suggest that Henry passes me the kitchen towel which is right by him and he goes and warns everyone not to enter the kitchen for a little while as I have had an accident. The smell is unbearable and I try to work as quickly as I can to disinfect the area. The infected kitchen towels I put into a plastic bag and without shame take it outside and put it in the bin. Next I need to see to myself and command that the shower be free otherwise heads will fall. I clean as much off myself as I can before announcing that I am coming upstairs naked. There is no sign of anybody around. Soon the vile smell will be changed to the fresh fragrance of rose petal.

Oh Lord, I came into this world naked, without blemish, perfect in every way, completely unaware of my vulnerability. Father, help me accept the raw nature of mankind and all that it throws at me, changing what I can and being peaceful about what I cannot.

I try once again to start my day. Having washed and put on clean clothes, but still pantless, I go once again to the utility room. It appears that the clean and not so clean washing has been put on, all of it! Bob has started breakfast and looks at me kindly. I say thank you to him. From his pocket he produces some underwear. 'I believe you are looking for a pair of these, they are clean.'

I take them and disappear to the toilet and make myself more comfortable. Henry calls down and asks if it is safe to make an appearance. With the affirmative having been given the other three also trek into the kitchen and start to eat whatever is cooked and ready. The smell of bacon is gorgeous and I am starting to feel really hungry.

Oh Lord, smell is such a wonderful sense. To be able to breathe in and out an aromatic fragrance that can inject a feeling of wellbeing, and later a memory to be reflected on, is truly incredible. Father help me to build up memories for my family that will bring them joy and laughter throughout their life when times of reflection prompt those moments.

Having woofed down their breakfasts like a hungry pack of lions, even Gabby manages a bacon sandwich much to my surprise, the troupe prepares their lunch boxes. Henry helps Lily Pink make a sandwich and leaves the bread out for Johnny and Gabby to makes theirs. All sorts of jars are left lying around the kitchen with knives sticking out of them. Gabby sorts out Johnny's otherwise she knows that there will be nothing left for her. Her hair is still a little on the pink side but only if you are looking for it. She looks at me and I look away, I don't want her to think I am surveying the aftermath of yesterday's disaster. A jumble of feet scramble for school shoes and then a lot of goodbyes are sent my way. Suddenly Bob appears suited and booted and gives me a quick peck on the cheek and with that the door opens and closes and then silence. I look at the state of the kitchen and smell burning, toast burning to be precise, but I cannot see anything in the toaster. However my attention is drawn to the hob where the bread was left from the sandwich making. I try to pick up the plastic packaging and strings of melted fine fibre cling to the bread. Where the hole is the bread has started to burn! Even though the smell and the mess are an inconvenience I find there is beauty in the tangled matter before me.

Oh Lord, help me to focus on the beauty of things and to be able take something positive from a situation even when it presents itself in a negative form.

When the hob is cold I shall attempt to deal with the situation. In the meantime I put the breakfast plates, cups and bowls into the dishwasher. Bob would prefer that I wash up instead of using the machine, but today I am going to use the thing as it is there. How convenient it is to have something else to wash my dirty dishes, to deal with the slops and stains of my household.

Oh Lord, rain down on me; let your drops splatter in all the areas of my life that need healing. Father, when the thunderstorms rage overhead cover me with your spiritual umbrella so that all evil forces may be kept away and I may be free to love and worship you.

My next stop is to get the vacuum cleaner out from underneath the stairs and run it over the carpets throughout the house. The door appears to be a little stuck as I pull on it, so I give it a gusty heave and its contents spill out all over me. Coats, shoes, hoover, toolbox, sewing container, plastic bags full of who knows what and a bookcase. Bookcase? What is that doing in there? How did whoever put it in there manage to do so in the first place? And then it struck me, my foot is underneath it. Pain begins to creep up to my brain and then a scream comes out of my mouth.

'Aaaaaaaaaah! Flinking bookcase. What idiot put that in there?'

There is of course no answer, only silence from the walls. In order to relieve my pain I have to take the offending item off my toe and stand it in the hallway. This enables me to hop about and get a good few choice words off my chest. Now I can see why the coats had been on the floor decorating the vacuum cleaner as the racking has broken due to the excessive use and overcrowding of materials placed on its old and fragile frame.

Oh Lord, You carried a heavy cross on your broken frame. Your weak and depleted body stumbled and fell underneath its weight. Father, I stumble under the weight of material possessions, help me to carry only what is essential to my spiritual growth and to declutter anything that might be toxic to my life and welfare.

I go, limping, to look for the electric drill and find that it is missing from its spot. So what's new? I return to the pile of coats and throw them onto the bookcase. Shoes end up the same way. The toolbox I return to the cupboard and push it to the back, along with my sewing container which I place on top. The plastic bags I leave in the hallway, but am intrigued as to what is in them. There are some newspapers going back to our teen days. But they all seem to have one theme, Paul Fraxton, Bob's old Headmaster. The articles are about fraud. As I read them a story unfolds of how the Head teacher had managed to leave the country with a large amount of money in his bank account, taken from the school's budget. He had been siphoning it off for years. But there was also a suspicion that he had been a little heavy handed with corporal punishment on the school boys in his care and one name hit me immediately, Robert Sponge. No wonder he didn't want to talk about his old Headmaster.

Oh Lord, we cannot do anything about our past to change it, but help us forgive the wrongs done to us and to find peace in the present by allowing your Spirit to take control of those areas that are broken.

Now I want to know what the news was about last Wednesday to do with Paul Fraxton. In order to do this I go online and type in 'news' and his name. It doesn't take long for the story to pop up. An older man than in the newspaper I have just read stares at me. He has returned to this country wanting to give himself up for the crime he had committed years earlier. Apparently he has spent all of the money and suddenly feels guilty for what he has done. But as I read the article it becomes clear that Paul Fraxton is suffering from cancer and believes that the best medical care is in England. Could that be the reason for his sudden sense of doing the right thing? The man does indeed look ill.

Oh Lord, you never give up on us; your hand is always waiting no matter how long we take to come to that decision to reach out and grasp it. Father help me to take those opportunities to grab hold of you no matter how big or small my need is.

With my inquisitive nature now satisfied I close down the computer and go back to the plastic bags. They must have been brought down from the loft, so I return them placing each just inside the roof space so that they are easily retrieved. My toe is really giving me a lot of pain, so I decide to put the hoover back under the stairs and nurse my digit by putting a bag of peas in a towel with the intention of sitting down with my feet up. I manoeuvre myself around the bookcase, coats and shoes and sit in my favourite reclining armchair. As I stare around the room, I see a slight crack in the wall, some cobwebs in the corner over the television, a stain on the carpet, a dirty bowl on the coffee table and a sock dangling from a picture on the wall! Perhaps sitting down and taking the weight off my feet wasn't such a good idea as now I can see other jobs that need to be done? Oh Victoria, let the chatter stop in your head, allow a bit of quiet to seep in and blinkers to take your mind off seeing chores.

Oh Lord, my mind is busy with so much, calm my business and allow me to sit at your feet.

It doesn't take long before our cat decides that I have made a nice comfy spot for her to lie on. She pads on my chest and dribbles contentedly. Stroking her is relaxing and I realize just how crowded my day is with invisible lists of things to do. A passing thought floats by but I allow it to drift off without exploring it in detail. A sense of peace descends on me as I sink into a meditative state. The room seems to be changing into a meeting place, there are twelve men sitting around a table all discussing different topics. Then the head of the table stands up and raises his hands. The room becomes silent and all eyes are on the tall, tanned, dark haired man whose eyes speak only of love and compassion.

'My time with you all is coming to an end my dear friends. Soon you will weep for me but what you see will only be the beginning.'

Worried faces stare at each other.

'What does he mean?' is expressed by several of the companions.

'Let us celebrate this last meeting with a meal my friends.'

137

I can see bread and wine being distributed amongst the group. The host holds both the food and the drink and looks at each of his disciples.

'Before the day is out this bread will be broken and this wine will be spilt.'

A voice says, 'No'.

The reply is gentle and firm, 'Trust me.'

The moment leaves me as I hear banging on the window beside me.

Oh Lord, my life is full of questions and often long pauses before answers become visible. How many times have I missed the right road because I have been too impatient to wait for your answer? Father help me to sit back and to Trust.

It takes me a moment to become fully awake from my dream state. Once functional again I hobble to the front door trying to balance the towel with the bag of peas in on my foot. Here I am greeted by the window cleaner. He wants his money especially as he has missed me the last two times. I offer a cheque but it is declined as the man wants cash. Unfortunately after a concerted effort to mimic a high wire artist balancing on one foot in the air and hopping on the other I retrieve my handbag only to find that I do not have enough money. I give him what I have and make a note of how much I still owe him. He is not that happy with this conclusion, but it is the best I can do. He says that he will only clean half the windows and the other half will be finished when the debt has been paid in full. I give him Bob's business card and suggest that he calls the number on it if he has any more grievances. It says 'Bob Sponge, Inventor and Computer Specialist, any problem you can't solve hand it over to the Expert. No problem big or small turned away.' He looks at it and humphs.

Oh Lord, what if you decided only to create half a person, or half a world. Which half would you pick?

True to his word the window cleaner does exactly that. I sit and watch him clean the bottom half of the living room windows. I have to say that I am impressed with his immaculate straight line running horizontally across the four window panes. I am also wowed by the difference between the clean and the dirty halves. Perhaps we could start a new fashion statement in window dressing.

Oh Lord, you gave us two choices, right or wrong, for or against, rock or sand. We build our lives on these choices. Father help me not to get muddled between the two but to make the right choice as to which side I want to be on.

The throbbing from my toe takes on a new level and I really need to have something to distract me from its pain apart from a couple of Paracetamol and a dripping defrosted bag of peas. I decide that perhaps a bit of television might be called for, so I look around for the remote control. It is supposed to be in the holder on the side of my chair, but my hand feels nothing as I reach inside. A quick scan of the room and it is nowhere to be seen. It appears that whoever had it last took it for a walk. Now I have to make a decision, do I hunt for it or just sit. I decide to sit. But it starts to bug me that I don't know where it is. The feeling rises and becomes unbearable; I have to find out where it has been put. I discard the soggy towel and feel down the creases inside the chair, then the settees (we have two of them), nothing, perhaps under the seating, again nothing, maybe in the coffee table drawers? It appears everything else has been stuffed in them but not the remote. The searching has made me feel upset; all I want is the controller to turn the TV on. I decide to give up and go to the toilet instead. As I sit relieving myself, I look at the books on the little book shelf opposite me. Bob likes to have something to look at while he is performing his duties, and there sitting on top of 'Essential Scrabble Words' is the lost remote. Now I know why Bob is so good at scrabble. He swots up on words in this little room!

Oh Lord, the lost shall be found, but then again in this house the lost often remains lost until I stop looking!

Now I can sit and watch a bit of telly. There are numerous programmes about relationship problems, selling or buying a house, police documentaries from around the world, airport customs and the problems they have with passengers trying to bring illegal items into that country and Children's TV. I opt for Children's TV as I have enough experience of relationship problems and need something light to watch. As I gaze at the purple, yellow, orange and red blobs that have hands and feet I wonder about the educational value of the programme, especially as I can't understand a word of what the creatures are trying to say. They seem to be in a hurry to do something but I can't quite make out what. Then they bump into each other and fall down. I decide that whatever they are attempting to teach is beyond me and so I change channel.

Oh Lord, isn't it funny how we run about in circles not knowing quite what we are supposed to be doing, until we seek guidance and ask you to show us what purpose you have for us. Father you made me with a purpose in mind, you gave me talents and gifts to help me search for your meaning in my life, help me to look in the right direction and accomplish your will for me.

'Would you buy this house? Well let's see if our couple are going to.'

Two rather dissatisfied clients seem to be at odds with each other as to whether they like the house or not and the cheery presenter asks them what they think. I was hoping that one of them would say, 'It is a dump and why did you bring us here?' But no such luck. Both are very diplomatic and say in a roundabout way, 'It is very nice but just not for us.'

So that's that then, no sale. I didn't need to see the whole programme to know the answer. I switch to another channel.

'And do you think this child is yours?' I press the button again.

'He looks very suspicious to me, he won't make eye contact.' I try another channel.

'Is that a fruit?' an airport official asks sternly.

'No it is for my consumption,' A Chinese lady replies in broken English.

'But is it a fruit?'

'It won't be when I have eaten it.'

140

'But you haven't eaten it yet.'

'Well that's because you won't let me.'

'You have been told about bringing fruit into this country, so I will have to confiscate it and give you a fine.'

'Not if eat it now.'

'Madam you know the rules.'

Before the two come to blows I switch the television off. I sigh; the world of confrontation can stay in the box, so much for a little relaxing entertainment.

Oh Lord, it seems that the world of media is rife with bringing disaster, anger, dissatisfaction and confrontation into our front rooms. No wonder our lives are so stressful. Father I need your help to bring peace into my home so that it is a haven from the stress of the outside world.

For some reason my stomach is beginning to make noises that resemble a plumbing problem with the radiators. I look at the time and realise that the morning has passed extremely quickly and it is indeed lunch time. I ponder a moment thinking about what I shall eat for lunch. Having decided on a cheese sandwich with a cup-a-soup, I rise from my reclineable chair and step directly onto the bag of peas that has come adrift from the towel. Just as I hit it there is a loud bang and peas explode all over the place, flying into corners, under furniture and behind any awkward gap impossible to retrieve from. It is amazing how many peas there are in a bag. Lunch is going to have to be cancelled until I have cleaned up. My only problem is how I get from my position to the dust pan and brush as I am surrounded by peas.

Oh Lord insurmountable odds are your forte. Nothing is impossible for you.

With an almighty hop I manage to do an Olympic record leap. Well it feels like that. In fact it is probably only a glimpse of what an athlete can achieve, but the momentum takes me up and over the majority of the peas and I land on my good foot, only to fall backwards from whence I came. The peas are now mushy and have no doubt made an impression on the back of my white sweatshirt. The carpet being green anyway will no doubt survive after a clean, but I was hoping that I could avoid that. It seems that I have made a worse mess.

Oh Lord my life is littered with good intentions. I admire your continued belief in our attempts no matter what the outcome. Father you are truly amazing.

Vicki, it is you that are amazing, I am so proud of how you keep going no matter what. Your courage and persistence carrying your cross of life is priceless. Be proud of your achievements my love, I am.

Afternoon Prayer

The telephone rings and it is Becky the Preschool leader. She is asking all members of staff to attend a debriefing of the Ofsted inspection this afternoon at two. This leaves me with a bit of time to sort out the pea problem, get some lunch and get changed. I decide that the best solution is to use the hand held vacuum cleaner and a bucket, as using a dustpan and brush will probably crush them or send them flying again as they are defrosting by the moment. As it scoops up the loose peas I am able to make a path in order to move through the sea of green. I avoid the puddle of mushy peas and turn left on my hands and knees looking for any that have run under the furniture. It is a slow process and I realise that I am going to have to move things in order to do a thorough job and time is running out. Those that are in the compact cleaner I unload into the bucket. The squashed peas are troubling me as they are going to need careful handling, so I limp into the kitchen and find the freezer spatula. With gentle scooping actions of the spatula I take off the worst of the splattered items and again use the bucket to put them in. It is all I have time for and now even lunch is off the menu as I need to get to the meeting.

Oh Lord, crushed and broken as I am you are always gentle with your handling of my life. You may have to prune hard at times, but it is always with our growth in mind that you tend to our Souls. No matter what mess I make with handling things you will always be there to pick up the pieces if I ask you to.

With the help of the banister I make it up the stairs and get changed. The back of my sweatshirt is certainly a sight, although I can actually see a lovely design which has been imprinted by the collision of force and peas. I am sure no artist has managed to come up with such an imaginative creation. However it needs to be consigned to the washing machine and its artistic memory of the event cleansed. Sad to say it will not be hung in the Tate Modern.

Oh Lord, beauty is in the eye of the beholder. What one beholds as a creation of chaos, others will see as a monument to artistic genius. Father how incredible is our own perception of life. Grant me the eyes to see through the obvious and discover the realms of eternal creation, where you delight in every one of us.

Ready with clean apparel I attempt the stairs again. I realise that I will have to wear sandals as my toe won't fit into my shoes. I have decided that walking is not an option, so I take the car, which is a crime to the ozone layer, as the Preschool is only a minute or two away. But then I need to be kind to myself.

Oh Lord, thank you for reminding me that I am important too.

As I enter the Preschool, there is food on the table and the smell of bacon, sausages and mushrooms fills the air. Becky has treated us to the butcher's delight, cooked meat baps. My mouth waters and my stomach rumbles for food. I am greeted with many questions as to what I have done to my toe as it stands naked in the light. I am promptly told to sit down and rest it. I love these people, who are so considerate and kind. A bap is placed in front of me and I inhale its tempting aroma. I want to dive in and eat, but refrain until everyone is seated and duly presented with their portion. We then bow our heads and thank God for our meal, friendship and preschool.

Oh Lord, there is nothing greater than true friendship, the giving and receiving, the helping and supportive nature of a band of friends, all united working to help each other to reach their destiny, a destiny with you at its centre. Father help me to fulfil your will in all areas of my life.

It seems that everyone is hungry not just me and our attention is on the food and savouring the delicious burst of flavours that tantalize our taste buds. Of course we are also eager to hear how we have done in the last two days under the watchful eyes of the Ofsted Inspectors. Juice dribbles down my chin and without a thought I wipe it away, not realising that it has also gone down my blouse as well. Becky hands me a piece of kitchen towel and smiles, she has managed to do the same thing too. We burst out laughing, and it becomes infectious. The height of the ceiling allows the merriment to fill the building.

Oh Lord, we raise our voices to you, may our joy sparkle amidst the heavenly host.

We wash down our meal with a glass of wine and then we get down to the serious business. Becky reports that the Inspection went very well, and we are to be commended for our quality of care. All members of the team were seen as exceptional practitioners and the management extremely strong. There were no areas of concern and all in all the Ofsted Inspectors were happy to give the Preschool an unofficial outstanding result. A clap starts to form, growing into a momentous accolade for our leader; we stand up and applaud Becky. Then she rises and returns the praise, in turn we hug and congratulate each other and then we are silent as we know that the praise and the glory belongs to God as we have worked under His banner for His honour. Becky offers a prayer of thanksgiving as each one of us has contributed without question or hesitation, doing our utmost in our work and from this earthly recognition God has been glorified. We are all elated, knowing that our service is outstanding to the children in our care.

Oh Lord, You have always given your creation outstanding care, no matter how difficult or unreceptive we are and have been throughout history. Thank you for your continual care and help me to emulate your example, not for myself but for your honour and glory, so that Your Kingdom may come here on earth.

As a thank you Becky announces that we shall have a staff outing one evening in the next month after the official announcement of the Ofsted report. This news is greeted with great enthusiasm as we all like a knees up. As the staff start to put away the chairs and table and sort out the washing up, Avril, the deputy, comes over with the first aid box and sits next to me. She asks if she can attend to my toe and I accept gratefully. As she applies a bandage and uses another toe as a splint I tell her about the pea incident. Avril can't help but laugh; it is a funny story when it is told in hindsight. Indeed it gets funnier the more it is told as each of my friends want to hear about my accident. Avril says that the only thing missing is me not wearing my Goofy hat!

Oh Lord, I hope Heaven is full of laughter as it has such a wonderful effect on our spirit.

Now with my toe supported and cushioned it is easier to walk on. With the tidying done everyone starts to make a move at going home. For the Preschool the week is over; we have closed another chapter of the book, knowing that a new beginning happens again on Monday. My friends will be busy over the weekend, catching up with chores and taking time to be with their own family. As we each make our way out of the door we hug and kiss our goodbyes and I offer Avril a lift home as she lives just around the corner. Once in the car Avril asks how I will cope with sorting out the bookcase and I tell her that I shall get the heavies onto it. Then she asks about the pea problem and again I reassure her that Bob, Vanish and the scrubbing brush will resolve it in the interim. Within moments we are outside her house, we wish each other a fun filled weekend and Avril disembarks from the car. Just as I signal to pull out from the curb, Lily Pink's bus overtakes me. Ten past three, where does the time go?

Oh Lord, time is such a phenomenal concept, when we have too much we don't know what to do with it and when we have too little we are complaining about the lack of it. What fickle beings we are. Father you are the master of time help me to use it wisely and to be a good manager of its totality.

As I get out of the car my daughter appears and looks at my strapped foot.

'What have you done this time mum?' she asks sympathetically.

I explain about the bookcase and she raises her eyes to heaven as though she will find an answer there as to why I seem to be accident prone. On opening the front door I start to warn Lily Pink about the state of the living room carpet, but before I can finish, she has slipped past me and entered the danger zone.

'What on earth?' is followed by a momentous flip that takes LP up and over and ends with a thud on her front. Her face says it all.

'And you call me accident prone?' I laugh.

I help Lily Pink stand up and remove her pea sodden clothing. She rushes upstairs to wash her face and hands and to put on her all-in-one. These always remind me of the romper suits the children had when they were babies. Then she finds a piece of paper and writes a warning sign. It is in big red letters saying 'Danger War Zone, Peas attacking, enter at your own risk'.

Oh Lord, how can one bag of peas cause so much trouble? Perhaps this is what is

146

called the Domino Effect? Father, your Son experienced this occurrence during his life on earth. One event led to another, and ultimately it ended with the Cross. Thank you Father that the domino effect did not end there in its earthly conclusion but continued on to the Glorious Resurrection fulfilling your love for us.

My thoughts go to the preparation of the evening meal, but Lily Pink wants to know when the living room will be cleaned up so that she can watch the television. I suggest that this inconvenience can be put to good use in the form of doing her homework. She gives me one of her disdainful looks. Lily Pink informs me that she only has spellings to do.

'Well, only spellings can be done now,' I respond firmly.

'But I don't want to do them now, it is Friday, I have all weekend to learn them,' my daughter argues.

I intend to win this altercation and as I know that LP likes competitive tasks, I suggest that by the time she has written them out ten times I shall have made a chocolate cake. It works and now I am up against it as a cake takes twenty-five minutes to cook in the oven and that is without the preparation time.

Oh Lord, the odds are against me, why do I do this? Why do I try to beat impossible odds in order to be the winner? How often have I decided to beat you to the finishing post? How often have I decided that because you are not doing what I want, I shall do the task in hand to show you how to do it? How silly is that? How often do I try to be God? Father you are God, a humble God who watches us as we play these games. Thank you Father that you understand our impatience, our meddling hands that produce answers that are momentary instead of waiting for Your solution that will procure a longer lasting remedy.

I realise that my toe is going to stop me whizzing around the kitchen, so I pop my head into the dining room and say to Lily Pink that the bet is off. She looks very disappointed, so I tell her the reason for my dilemma and say that it is an unfair challenge. LP agrees and jumps off her chair thinking that she has got away with not doing her homework.

'Where are you going?' I enquire.

'To help you make the cake,' she smiles. A clever diversion tactic from my daughter, so I compromise and say that she can help me when she has written her spellings out five times instead. She groans but decides that five times is better than ten and returns to her homework.

Oh Lord, compromise is such a helpful tool when dealing with everyday matters. But in matters of the soul you show that there can be no compromise. Help me Father not to compromise my soul.

Baking a cake with Lily Pink is always an experience as she loves to weigh and mix the ingredients then she throws everything in together and whisks enthusiastically. She doesn't have time to sieve the flour from a height, allowing the air to breathe through the fine particles as I do. The funny thing is, the end result is usually a success! The chocolate ends up in the mix as well as in her mouth, but I turn a blind eye to this as she is having a lovely time. It is so pleasing to be able to share time together with my youngest creating a mouth-watering dessert.

Oh Lord, there is a time for everything, and these moments are so precious. Help me Father to make time to just enjoy such impromptu occasions.

With the cake cooking and the arrival of the other members of the family, I turn to the preparation of the main meal. But my thoughts are disturbed by the conversation coming from the hallway.

'But I just want to see.'

'No Johnny,' a younger voice exclaims, 'can't you see the sign I put up?'

'I just want to pop my head around the door to see the pea invasion.'

'Mum, Johnny's gone into the living room,' an exasperated voice calls out.

'I can't see any peas Lily Pink.'

'Ohhh you are standing in them!'

'Oops. Sorry.'

'And now you have trod them into the hall carpet too with your clod hopping big shoes.'

'Sorry, again.'

'MUM!' Lily Pink yells.

I sigh and open the Kitchen door. 'Never mind love, just put something over the top of the mess and it will get cleaned up later.'

'Can't you do it now mum?'

I say no as I am trying to get on with the dinner.

Oh Lord, perfector of multi-tasking, grant me the resources I need to juggle the many tasks I have to perform.

I like to have fish on a Friday, so I look for the ingredients for a fish mash. As I am peeling the potatoes Gabby enters the room. She asks if she can help and I refrain from commenting on the rarity of the occasion, instead I hand her the peeler and start to cut up the fish into small pieces. We work together quietly until Gabby decides to tell me what is on her mind.

'The pink hair thing mum,' she starts. 'It was something I just wanted to try and I know that you are not happy about me dyeing my hair. I was going to do it after I had discussed it with you at the weekend. I really did mix up the bottles last night as I had water in my eyes and couldn't see what I was doing.'

I just listen as I don't want to interrupt her flow.

'My friend Aisha; it was her house we went round to yesterday. Last time I visited them, her mother felt that you were a bit old fashioned from the things I have said in the past. I suppose you are when compared to her. Well you saw what she is like, very modern. She believes that girls ought to be allowed to experiment and find their own image. I mean it is not a bad thing that you are old fashioned, I love you for who you are, but sometimes I just would like a little bit more

149

freedom to make choices and to discover for myself what is right or wrong rather than you just telling me.'

I ponder her words and know that she is saying some very important things to me. I need to trust her more as she is growing up into a beautiful, intelligent young woman. I gaze at my daughter, and admit that we are never too old to learn, in fact as far as girls growing up are concerned I am a novice and I needed my teenager to show me this.

Oh Lord, how clever I am at expressing my view point and making out that I am an expert in all known fields because I have lived fifty years. Father it has taken a fourteen year old to show me how little I really know of life. Gracious Father it is not easy to accept that I am wrong. Help me to reappraise my thought patterns so that I may allow others to express their opinions and wisdom. Thank you for this lesson.

As Gabby mashes the cooked potatoes I apologise for my lack of understanding of her needs. She is right I need to stand back and allow her space to explore her world, which is so different to the one I grew up in. My knowledge is outdated, and she needs to be able to cope in a new world with greater challenges with my background support, rather than my disapproving attitudes to 'today's youngsters' and their young mothers. We take out the cake and pop the fish pie into the oven and make up a salad.

Gabby turns to me and says, 'Thank you.'

I feel that it is me who should say the thank you and I tell her so. She plants a little kiss on my cheek.

'What no air kiss?' I tease and she smiles.

'Can I have my belly button pierced?'

Gabby sees the horror on my face and laughs. I take a deep breath, as I realize that it was a joke. 'It was a joke Gabs, wasn't it?' She looks at me and winks. I am not sure where I stand with that last statement!

Oh Lord, enough surprises please, little steps would be the kindest thing for me at the moment.

I am expecting Bob any moment and I am not disappointed as he opens the front door on time. The food is ready, steaming on top of the oven waiting to be dished up. I ask Bob to summon the children, which he does in full volume at the bottom of the stairs. Then he wanders off to get changed and I think to myself, why didn't he just knock on their doors as he went to our bedroom and tell them that dinner is ready? I am mystified by this detail. Maybe this is what his mother did as Bob tended to spend hours in the shed at the bottom of the garden when he was a child. There he would make model aeroplanes and act out battles for his ever growing army. Perhaps yelling was her only way to make herself heard over his battle cries.

The girls arrive first but there is no sign of Henry and Johnny. I suggest that Gabby and Lily Pink start to dish up fairly between the six of us, fairly being the important word and I head up to Henry's room. I knock, silence, I knock again.

'Who is it?' Henry asks.

'Your mother,' I express in a quiet tone.

'What do you want?'

I tell him dinner is getting cold.

'We will be down in a minute,' he replies.

I enquire if Johnny is with him and he confirms that he is. I ask tentatively what he is doing.

'Nothing,' is the response.

I am not convinced, but decide to leave it there. I suggest that they don't leave dinner for too long otherwise it will be cold.

Oh Lord, how often have you knocked on my door and I have been too busy to open it to you. Father help me to answer Your call when you knock, and not to be too consumed with my affairs to ignore Your presence.

As Bob, Gabby, Lily Pink and I are eating our culinary delight, Henry and Johnny make an entrance. My first reaction is to close my mouth as it is ajar. Gabby is the first to speak.

'What do you two look like?' she chuckles. Then a light bulb moment happens to my daughter.

'You've been at my makeup!' she screams.

'Only the stuff you threw in the bin,' Henry retorts.

Gabby relents.

The two boys sit down at the table and pretend that all is normal. Bob finds it very hard to have a conversation with two female looking boys. Then he decides that a statement needs to be made.

'If you two ladies are going to eat at my table, then the least you can do is eat like gentlewomen, your manners are appalling.'

Henry apologises and raises his little finger in the air as he tries to scoop up the fish sauce on his plate with his fork. I look at Henry and Johnny.

'Why?' I ask.

Henry answers for both of them. 'We just wanted to know what it is like wearing this stuff and why girls make such a fuss about painting their faces. It takes forever and look at the state of us. Has it improved our features?'

I am stumped as to what to say, but Lily Pink joins in and comments.

'Quite frankly you both look ridiculous and that is why make up is for girls not for boys.'

Johnny pipes up next and says that it is like wearing a face mask. Why would anyone want to hide behind it? He looks unhappy for a moment, as I realise that Johnny must identify with this state of being. He asks Henry if he can take it off now as he feels very uncomfortable. Having finished their meal, the pair disappear.

Oh Lord, it is so easy to wear a mask, not to show our real selves to others. But You see through the mask and ask us to bear all to You. The risk is I will be too afraid, so Father help me to be true to who I am and not to be afraid to show my real self to You and the world.

Dearest Vicki, you know who I Am, allow me to show you off to the world as my adored daughter. I will protect your vulnerability and make you strong.

Trust me.

Evening Prayer

Bob and I clear the table of plates and together we wash the dishes. I tell Bob about the state of the living room and ask if he could very kindly apply his muscle power to cleaning the carpet. He agrees and I am extremely grateful. I have to say that he is the king of carpet cleaners. Nothing stands a chance when he gets his hands on a messy job. I do warn him however of the loose peas and he assures me that he will take care. Bob then discusses the bookcase in the hallway and asks if he should move that once he has finished in the living room. I say yes but that it isn't to go back under the stairs.

Oh Lord, thank you for my husband, for my helper and companion. Thank you that I have someone to share things with. Bless our union.

Knowing that I can leave everything to Bob I can now start to think about this evening, Friday evening. I have waited the whole week, looking forward to spending time with my friends. It is a monthly treat where a group of mothers get together and socialise. But I am not sure how much activity I am going to be able to do with my toe. Taking the car I swing by Cathy's house to see if she is coming out with the gang from the mother's prayer group. When she opens the door, she looks troubled and ready to cry. I feel a knot in my stomach as I didn't returned her phone call last night, nor managed to fit a visit in during the day. I hobble back to the car and lock it and then I follow Cathy into her house.

Oh Lord, lift up those who are weighed down.

She heads straight for the kitchen and puts the kettle on, she asks me if I want tea or coffee and I realise that my bowling evening may well be cut short as my friend needs me to be near her. I decide on coffee and accept a cake, although I shouldn't really as my scales will protest at this. We take our supplies in to the living room and I take a seat next to Cathy. I can see that she wants to cry but is holding it in, trying desperately not to let the tears flow. As soon as I put my hand on her shoulder the gates open and the resolve is forgotten. I look for some tissues and see none so I nip out to the kitchen to find a box. There on the table I see a note, open, right by the tissues. All it says is, 'Sorry, I

154

can't go on.' A feeling of dread fills me. I return to the living room and give Cathy a handful of Kleenex and hug her tightly. There is no need for words yet as I know they will come when they are ready.

Oh Lord, great are your mighty deeds and your majesty. How awesome your wisdom. No situation is too large for your compassion and love. Father, this situation here and now feels too enormous for me to deal with, help me to know what to do and say.

There is a ringing close by, it makes us both jump. It appears to be coming from my bag. I very rarely have a mobile phone on me as I don't actually own one. However tonight I had asked Bob earlier if I could take his just in case I needed to be contacted for any reason. I don't even know how to use it, which shows how little I know of this type of technology. It stops but then starts again, so I take it out and look at it, put it to my ear and say hello. Nothing, well of course not it helps if you turn it on! I look at the thing as if it is alien, and Cathy takes it off me and presses something and hands it back. She mouths 'talk', so I do and it is Bob wondering why I am not at the Bowling Alley. I briefly tell him where I am and ask him to let the girls know that I won't be going tonight after all. He hangs up and I fumble around trying to find an off switch and Cathy comes to my aid again.

Oh Lord, I lift my hands to you in prayer, thank you God that it is easy to communicate with you.

The interruption seems to have jolted my friend out of her tearful zone. She is now prepared to tell me the frightful truth of the letter.

'James has committed suicide.' Her statement is blunt and to the point. I look her in the eyes and say how sorry I am. It feels inadequate and my mind races to think of something more to say.

All I can think of is, 'When? How? Oh Cathy, that is awful!'

She tells me that he left a note and the police gave it to her this morning. He had been found in the grounds of the hospital hanging from a tree.

'Where is God now?' she asks.

Oh Lord and God, when we lose hope and are paralysed by fear, help us not to lose sight of you. Give us the courage to reach out for your hand, because in all things you are faithful to us. In Your unfailing love help Cathy, and help me too to silence the doubts when they come.

I take Cathy's hand in mine. 'God is still here with us, he never leaves us no matter how low we get.'

Then I remember the time in the Bible where Jesus is led into the wilderness by the Spirit. There he is tempted for forty days and forty nights by the devil. And to all of these tests, in his weakened state, Jesus refers to the Scriptures, God's Holy Word, for His answers, ultimately saying to the last temptation, 'You must not test the Lord Your God.' I gently tell Cathy that she is being tempted in her sorrow and anger to question her faith in God, to blame God for James taking his life. In her weakness the only answer can be God, as only he can heal her pain and abandonment. However it is human to be angry, to feel resentment, to want to yell at God and that is alright as He is big and strong and has huge shoulders to bear our insults and pain. He understands, He knows, He ultimately cares and He wants to carry us during this time. Now is the time to reach out and take His hand and to Trust, even though Cathy doesn't want to, even though every sinew in her body is screaming no, go away, leave me alone!

Oh Lord, sometimes only screaming will do as we try to express our anger at a situation that seems so unfair, so disproportionate to the matters at hand. Father so often our humanness fails as we cannot see the end of the road as it takes us where we do not want to go. When this happens Father help us, help me to Trust in Your Glory, and in Your Victory so that our/my faith remains firmly in Your Kingdom.

I continue to try to console Cathy. 'Our Father would have been with James in his hour of need. You know that James was very ill and could not be accountable for his actions. Jesus knows this too and has already pleaded with the Father to forgive James, as he did on the cross when he spoke the words, "Father forgive them for they don't know what they are doing." God's heart is always open to our cries.'

Oh Lord, how often do we not know what we are doing? Thank you that you love us so much that in our frailness you continue to adore us, your creation, YES, adore me. I cannot praise you enough for your great Love.

'How is God going to help me now?' Cathy comments.

I pause and contemplate the answer. 'God is merciful Cathy; he is here now in the centre of your grief. Jesus stumbled and fell under the weight of His Cross. He was given help to carry it. He is there to help us carry our cross too if we face him and ask. His scarred hands are outstretched waiting for you to pour out your frustration, anger and feeling of desertion. God will understand your desolation, your abandonment. No other God knows and feels that same pain that you are witnessing right now. Only He can be your Saviour and Comforter and only He can bring you peace and healing in the times ahead.'

Cathy looks at me and turns away. 'He has let us down, God has let us down.'

Oh Lord, it is not easy to see the light when all around us is dark, when we feel overwhelmed with the enormity of a situation. How hard it is to pray, praise and dance during these times. But you never let us down, even if we can't lift our voices to you in prayer. Your loyalty knows no bounds, we are always your children and you are always there for us, for me.

I ask if she really feels God has let her down. She answers angrily, that he has and that he was supposed to save them from this terrible conclusion. Why didn't God show the doctors and nurses that James was thinking of committing suicide? Why would he leave her to pick up the pieces? Why did he take the easy way out? How could he be so selfish? Why did it have to happen to them, if only James had been stronger? I ask Cathy if she has told anyone else about James and she shakes her head. 'Not yet,' she replies and then tells me that the hospital chaplain came to see her on the ward when she went to collect James' possessions. He said he would organise things if she wanted him to, or at least make a few phone calls if she needed, to her pastor. Cathy sat quietly now that she had revealed her shocking news. It was out in the open, someone else knew; her life will no longer be the same. She is now a widow, on her own.

Oh Lord, blessed are those that mourn for they shall be comforted. Bless Cathy's anger, her disappointment, her crushed hopes, please bring goodness out of this darkness, and allow the sun to shine again when this period of Lent passes. Grant Cathy the strength to live again and to seek your face beyond the tomb.

I feel I have said enough. We both just sit, Cathy looks at her hands and I at the beautiful dolls house that is perched on a small table in the corner of the room. I think it a bit trivial but I ask about this feature in the room, as I don't think I have seen it before, or perhaps I just haven't noticed it there. Cathy glances over to the miniature; she sighs, and tells me that James had made it for her many years ago. He had painstakingly crafted furniture for it, in wonderful detail. He had waited for children to come into their life, but none had come and so the bedroom with the cot in had remained empty. Cathy felt that this was very symbolic and James had lost interest in making the doll's house into a home.

'It will never be finished now,' she concluded. 'My life feels as empty as the doll's house.'

Oh Lord, how painful change is, but with you there is always a beginning, middle and end. There is always Hope. Our lives may falter at times, but you show us that challenges are there to bring us closer to your own Story. Father help Cathy and help me to unite our life with Yours and to journey on with courage knowing that you have already walked this path yourself.

I look at Cathy and ask her if I can pray with her. She nods a yes and I cup her hands in mine and close my eyes. Aloud I pray:

'Oh Lord, when life just seems to be the nearest it can to a tragic end, the only place we can go is to the foot of your Cross and look into your eyes. Only there can we see hope, your Hope amidst the pain, suffering and bleakness of a desperate situation. Even in that cruel death you showed comfort to your mother giving her another son to take care of her when you have died. Blessed Jesus, you never leave us alone with our suffering, you are always there beside us holding our hand. What we see as darkness, you transform into light when we allow you to take charge of the situation. Calvary was death in all its awful glory; hopelessness personified, your earthly body naked, broken and distorted. What good could come from such a tragic end? Our Saviour dead, nailed to a tree, the material of your profession. But your journey did not end there, and neither does ours. Out of death, you arose. We too can now rise, transform the overwhelming power of helplessness and anger that this sudden death has brought. My God, deliverer from all evil, may your radiant Spirit take control of my friend's situation, give her courage to walk this path and to forgive the abandonment she now feels from being left alone to face her future. Praise you God for what has happened, be at its centre and protect your grieving daughter.'

Cathy breaks into tears and I embrace her. We are united in the grief of the women at the foot of the cross. We stare at the face of the crucified Son of God, lifeless, alone. I am aware that Cathy needs more support, and that I can't carry her on my own. I don't want to leave Cathy to use her landline so I attempt to use Bob's mobile phone. Using it is easier than I thought and I successfully contact Paula and ask if she can come round to Cathy's house. She agrees readily knowing that her friend is fragile at the moment. Paula arrives after ten minutes and puts on the kettle for a cup of tea. I inform Cathy that I just need to talk to Paula for a moment and she just sits staring at the doll's house. Paula is a great and Godly woman, and I feel stronger in her presence. She is sadden by the news of James' death but appears to know what to do, as she has had years of experience in Bereavement Counselling. I am glad that I called her.

Oh Lord, sometimes it is better to know our limitations and call on others for help in case we make things worse. Our good intentions can go awry. Jesus knew when to call on you, in his darkest hour he prayed for our forgiveness, he handed over our sins to you and your mercy. His moment of carrying us was almost over as his precious blood dripped onto the earth below his feet. The very earth that you had created was washed by his life giving force. The earth and all its inhabitants would never be the same. No other sacrifice would be sufficient as God's only son breathed his last. Father God by the blood of your Lamb we shall be healed, our sins washed away and the Victory won.

Paula takes a cup of tea in to Cathy and places it onto the coffee table. Then she notices the first cup that has not even been drunk. She asks Cathy why she hadn't called her when she had received the news about James. Cathy looked down at her feet.

159

'I was ashamed; I didn't want to admit that James had taken his life. I felt let down, confused, so many emotions took over that I couldn't think straight. Then I decided that if I didn't tell anyone James might not be on the slab in the mortuary.'

Oh Lord, denial can sometimes feel like the only way forward. Sometimes we prefer to put our heads in the sand instead of facing up to reality. It can be the flight or fight of survival. Father help me to be brave and to face up to things as and when they are presented to me.

Paula tells Cathy that she would like to take her to her home to take care of her during these early days, especially as Cathy has no family to call on. Cathy is not sure as she feels that there is a lot that needs to be done, things to be organised, a funeral to be arranged. But she agrees to go with Paula tonight as she does not want to be alone and is aware that I have other responsibilities that tie me up. I go and wash the cups, saucers and plates while Paula and Cathy go upstairs to pack an overnight bag. When they are finished, we turn the lights off in the house, lock the door and leave the empty house to its own thoughts. Once Paula has settled Cathy into the front seat of the car, she tells me not to worry about my friend and that she will keep me informed as to how Cathy is coping. I am relieved as Paula has the time and the skills to help my friend. As I get into my own car I suddenly realise how much energy this evening has sapped from my being. I feel totally exhausted, so much so that I start to shake. It has been an awful shock, and I don't feel able to drive the short distance home. Automatically I ring Bob and he picks up the house phone on the second tone and agrees to walk around and drive me back.

Oh Lord, I feel washed out, drained, and completely empty. That was really hard seeing my friend so distraught, flattened, and hopeless. Restore us please Father God.

I don't even have the energy to talk to Bob. He senses that I am too tired to share what has happened and just allows me to be. The house is relatively quiet, no one on a Friday evening goes to bed the same time as on a school day, but for once there seems to be a lack of movement or noise. Bob answers my silent question.

'They are all watching a movie round at Holly's. She has just hired Rat

Raiders and rang up to see if anyone wanted to watch it with her. Everyone including Johnny said yes.'

I have never heard of 'Rat Raiders' but Holly knows a good film when it comes out. She is a sweet older lady who adores my children as if they were her own grandchildren. Holly and her husband Ken adopted us when we first moved here. They had invited us in for a hot meal that first day as they could see that moving in with four children was going to be hard work. We have been firm friends ever since.

Oh Lord, thank you for those special friendships that help us through life, who love us no matter what. Father, you who shows us unconditional love help me to walk that extra mile for my friends when they need me most.

Bob is shocked when I tell him about James. He shakes his head and says that he didn't realise that Cathy's husband was so down, that he had walked so far into the valley of darkness. He hugs me and we stay close just holding one another.

'Poor Cathy,' Bob finally says, 'she is now all alone; they were devoted to one another. I can't believe it.'

I say that the church must support her now, be her family, comfort her and build her up to face life again. She needs to see and feel God working through their kindness and love to help restore her faith. In the rough waters that she faces now only God can reach her in his life boat. Only He can save her from drowning; his lifeguards will be fighting against the storm of confusion and rejection to throw her a life line, and I pray that she will be able to reach out and grab it. I thank God for Paula because she will be of great practical and spiritual help to Cathy in the days ahead. She understands the trauma of losing a loved one suddenly as she lost her husband to cancer in a short space of time, several years ago.

Oh Lord, our experiences however traumatic are canvasses of life; they can bring knowledge and help to others in time of need. Father, you are with us in our sufferings and hardships and you never desert us, it is us who desert you. Grant me the grace to keep my eyes on you always.

161

I tell Bob that I need to go to bed as I feel that I have given all I can today. My reserves are all gone. He agrees and offers to stay up until the brood come home. Before I go to bed I relax in a bath and just allow the water to calm my weary body and mind.

Oh Lord, take the experiences of today and bless them, for you are God Almighty, All Powerful God Head and Merciful Protector. Gather your children into your heart and give them rest. Grant me rest.

Vicki, my child, rest in my presence. Be at peace in my love.

Night Prayer

Alone in my bed with the night closing in and sleep almost upon me, I speak to my God.

Oh Lord, I offer up my day to you, it has been a privilege to walk with you today.

My dear Vicki, your 'yes' was so powerful today, thank you for sharing in my passion and death. Your compassion and witness gave me strength to continue to carry my cross on my journey to Calvary. The blessings that you gave with your generosity comforted me as I suffered at the hands of men who enjoyed crucifying an innocent man. You were there for me at the foot of the cross. You did not run away when you saw my tortured spirit. You brought me help when I needed it most and you placed me in the arms of a faithful servant who would look after my shattered body. Thank you.

I realise that Cathy was Jesus in human form. How often do we meet Jesus in our everyday lives and not realise that we are in His presence? That he is calling us to serve him by serving others, that when we do a service to our fellow neighbours, both known and unknown, we do it for Him. There are so many Calvary's, so many wounded and crushed people in our world, how can we not see Jesus in all this and help Him; help His beloved people?

Oh Lord, help me not to be blind to the needs of others. Help me not to be selfish and live in a goldfish bowl and only see my needs day in and day out. Help me to reach out and to touch your sacred scarred hands and to touch your wounded side. To bring comfort to those who cry out, no matter who they are. Give me your courage to stand and be counted as a true believer in Christ. To be among the Holy men and women who stood at the foot of your cross and stated 'We believe you are the Son of God.' Father help me to see when you are crying, aching, in pain and in need of comfort. Help me not to pass on the other side of the road, hoping that someone else will look after the needy.

Vicki my darling daughter, how proud I am of you. Your prayer has been heard and I am adding an extra ingredient to your mix, my raising agent. Your cake will now rise even higher and be

lighter than it has ever been before and although the cross that you carry each day is long and heavy I will always be by your side helping you carry it, lifting it when you fall and encouraging you to keep walking towards your destiny. Your walk is my walk, and together we will walk the walk of salvation.

Chapter Six

Saturday

Morning Prayer

'Anxiety weighs down the heart, but a kind word cheers it up.' – Solomon, King of Israel; Proverbs 12:25 (New International Version)

The phone clashes with my dream and I awake with a start. I look at my watch; it is three thirty in the morning. I climb over Bob to reach for the object of the intrusive noise and say hello. It is my mother and she is in a terrible state. My father has gone missing again; she has looked everywhere in the house and outside. I ask her how long dad has been missing and she says four hours. She has already contacted the police and appears to be on first name terms with them now. They have failed to find dad so far. Before she rings off she asks if I can possibly make the journey up to see her as she really needs some support. My mum very rarely asks for help so I know that this is important to her. How can I refuse? At this time of day it will only take two, maybe two and a half hours. I agree and she breathes a sigh of relief and says 'thank you'.

Bob is stirring due to the talking and asks what is going on. I inform him of the situation and he accepts that this is something I need to do for my mother. I quickly write down the chores for the day, pack a small bag and tip toe into each of the children's rooms to kiss them good bye. It is four o'clock.

Oh Lord, I say 'yes' to you again, even though I do not know what today holds, but Father I will need your support. Bless my journey and may it be uneventful. Enfold my mother in your arms and may she feel your Strength and Courage in her time of anxiety.

The weather is fresh which I would expect for a March morning and once in the car the drive is fast with few on the motorway. Although tired at being up so early I listen to the radio to keep myself alert. The miles speed by and by six thirty I am almost at my mother's house. I can see a police car outside and an ambulance too, but there is no sign of movement. I park my car on mum's drive in the space next to hers. The door is on the latch, and inside I can hear men's voices. As I open the front door all eyes turn to me, I smile as one policeman and two paramedics gaze at my entrance. They are all sipping tea in the kitchen. My mum is unable to see past the tall professionals and asks who it is. One of the paramedics says it is a lovely young lady, a vision for sore eyes.

'Then it can only be my beautiful daughter,' she replies.

I walk forward, past the men and hug my mum.

'Cup of tea love?' she enquires.

I accept and then turn to one of the policemen and ask if there is any news. None. It must be over seven hours since dad went missing.

Oh Lord, Your earthly mother and father knew how it felt to have lost you when you were teaching in the temple. Their anxiety was at its highest not knowing where you were. Please have pity on my mother as she awaits news of my father. You know where my father is, please reveal to the police his whereabouts and bring him home safe and sound.

The officer's radio breaks the moment. He walks through the hallway and out of the front door. My mother and I wait in silence holding hands. When he returns she asks Alf, the constable, if there is any news. He shakes his head and says that the message was about another ongoing situation. I ask the paramedics if they have been at my mother's house for long and they say they only arrived a few minutes before me. Usually they park up at the end of the road in the lay by waiting for an emergency call. As they were proceeding to their usual checkpoint Alf had waved them to stop and suggested that they stay here in the warmth and then if my father turned up they could be on hand to offer emergency aid if necessary. I ask what the chances are of a seventy eight year old surviving the night out in the open. They said that there was always hope, maybe he had found some shelter. Suddenly I remember dad's tag. Mum had insisted that he wear it around his neck. It had his name and address on it, like a dog collar and it was for precisely this type of situation. For when he wandered off and got lost. I ask her about the tag and mum responds that dad had ripped it off and said that it was an imposition on his freedom.

Oh Lord, sometimes we don't know what is best for us and we complain when our freedom is taken away, even when it is for our own good. Tagging you wouldn't have worked, as you needed your freedom to do Your Father's work. How sad that our age can cause us such distress. Father even when we are unable to walk freely and to do the everyday tasks due to declining health, help us, help me when the time comes, to be accepting of the frailties and to be kind to ourselves, to myself and to find that inner peace that You promise us.

I can just see my father expressing this comment, stating that he isn't a dog and doesn't need to be kept on a leash. But now I wish he had kept the tag on as he is lost without it, indeed we are lost without it too. The ambulance crew are summoned away and mum, Alf and I decide to have breakfast. Mum needs something to do so she makes us all a bacon sandwich and another cup of tea. It is now seven thirty. Alf radios in to see if there is any more news. Still nothing. He is told to stay with us until there is an outcome. Apparently the police have put an urgent message on the local television and radio network in order to help with the search. We go into the sitting room and turn on the news channel. After a few news items, a picture of my father appears on the screen, then a message is conveyed about him being missing and if anyone knows of his whereabouts to contact the following number.

Oh Lord, how easy it is for us to get lost and to walk the wrong path. Thank You Father that you don't need a tracking device to know where we are in our lives, as you are All Knowing and All Seeing. We are so loved by you that you know our every step, our every thought, our every decision. It is us, me, who walks away from your side by not seeking your will or listening to your plan for our daily lives. Forgive me Father for not looking at your road map for my life, for failing to see the directions that you have blessed my life with by wandering off on my own. Grant me a wise eye to see your glorious path that has meandered throughout my life, and continues to shape my road to Your Kingdom.

The morning drags by and even with the television advertising my father's plight there is still no news. My mother has hoovered the whole of the downstairs and is struggling to heave the vacuum cleaner up the stairs to start up there. She needs to keep busy otherwise her thoughts

167

will turn to darker ideas of what has happened to dad. Alf has gone off duty and so far we have been left to wait on our own, no doubt resources are tight for the police force and it feels that a sense of the inevitable is creeping into this situation. The phone rings and it is Bob, he is just checking to see how things are progressing and to tell me that everything is fine at home.

Oh Lord, waiting is so hard. Please may we hear something soon?

Bob hands the telephone over to Lily Pink as she wants to know all of the ins and outs of what is going on. She is upset that I hadn't awoken her to say goodbye in the early hours of this morning. She is full of the antics of the morning, how Johnny had fallen out of bed and cracked a plate that was on the floor of his room. I ask if he was unscathed by the incident and she replies that he has a big bottom and nothing could survive a collision with it. But did he get cut from the plate? I repeat. Apparently not Lily Pink continues. Gabby decided to try the pink creation again and it looks even brighter than last time, and LP got her sister to put a little bit in her hair too! Henry is still in bed and has declared that he intends on staying there until Monday morning. I can't see that happening as he will get hungry and Bob won't wait on him by trooping up and downstairs with food. So it appears that Saturday morning is in full swing in my household. When Bob returns to the phone he tells me that the chores are underway, well sort of, in fact if he were honest they are in the upper most part of his brain to be done, when he has time to figure out how to turn the washing machine on. I instruct him to ask Gabby as she knows what settings and how to divide the colours. That is when she has finished pinking herself. The phone call has cheered me up as it reminds me of the chaos of real life, well the chaos of my life. We say our goodbyes and I tell Bob that I will let him know as soon as anything happens.

Oh Lord, we are so different, each member of my household seeking to find their place in the family and in the wider world. What a joy it is to have diversity. Thank you father for my family, who keep me grounded and on my toes.

The hoover has suddenly gone quiet and I can hear muffled sobs from upstairs. My mother has finally given in to her anxieties and allows the tears to flow even though she tries to hide them from me. I go up and sit next to her on my parent's bed. However these days it is no longer shared by them both as dad has bad nights and mum needs her sleep, so my father uses the spare bedroom. There are no words to describe her worries. It is now twelve hours since dad went missing. It must be the longest they have been apart from each other, not including when my dad worked of course. They'd always enjoyed each other's company and did everything together. They didn't long to have days away from their spouse. They disagreed at times, but then that is only natural. Each were only children and I was their only child, so the family became very close, knitted by their need for each other's company. Now my mum is feeling alone, her partner of fifty eight years missing from her side and even though he has been absent in mind on and off for the last year due to his illness, he is still Fred to her, her lifelong sweet heart.

Oh Lord, blessed is my parents' marriage, a bond that has lasted over half a century, a vow that has been tested in health and in sickness. Your hand has been at the centre of their closeness, binding them to be one. This trinity of faith seeing them through a life time of joys and trials. Father please unite them once again.

'I just want him to come home,' my mum finally says.

Of course she does. Suddenly the face that has seen so many pictures looks tired and old. Her seventy five years taking its toll on her beautiful features. I realise that her hair is completely white, any trace of her dark glorious mane gone, not even a glimmer of colour at her roots, something I hadn't really noticed before, as the familiarity of my mum has blinded me over the years. Her frail body slumps forward as she puts her head in her hands.

'What am I going to do without Fred?' a tear drops down her cheek onto her skirt and blends into the wool.

My mother wipes the trail of damp with her handkerchief and looks at me. Her blue eyes are dewy. She wants to be strong, but the last year has taken its toll on her, physically and mentally, as she has struggled on her own to carry the burden of her husband's mental fragility. How I wish that I lived closer. I think she senses what I am thinking.

'You have been a wonderful daughter, you have a beautiful family. They

169

are your first call, and I really appreciate you being here with me now and for the sacrifice that this has meant for your family. I called and you came, thank you.' My mother is so kind.

Oh Lord, this waiting is so hard. Not knowing where my dad is. I feel I should be doing something to find him, but what? I know that when the time is right You will reveal to us the answers. Until then Father help me to stay strong and to praise You.

It seems like I spend my life running around trying to solve problems, to the extent that I don't like mysteries. A mystery means loose ends, no ending to a story, unfinished business, a crucifixion without a resurrection. I like life to be orderly, but for some reason my life is actually messy. There are times when I have too many balls in the air that I am trying to juggle, and the result is they end up all over the place. I wonder if this is how my father feels, his world has been turned upside down by his muddled thought processes. His life has become a mystery, no doubt a more fearful one that has become adrift from its moorings. Oh where is he?

Oh Lord, I seek your face in my confusion, I am looking but I cannot see you. Your closeness appears to be gone and I feel I am walking on my own. Where are you?

My mother has produced a photo album; it looks old and has been handled many times over the years. She opens the first page; there staring out at me is my mother and father on their wedding day. They look so young; my mother is dressed in a simple outfit with a funny little hat perched on her head. My father looks dashing in a suit with a red tulip in his button hole.

My mum muses. 'Your father chose this flower because the tulip signifies perfect love and the red colour symbolises warmth, passion and energy. He said I was his passionate love.'

And so she was, and still is. I do so admire their love. Mum smiles at the distant memory.

'We were so in love, we didn't have a penny, but we didn't care, we had each other, what more did we need?'

We looked through the pages; there weren't many photographs of the wedding, but those that were there were beautiful. Then came a long leap in years, eight in all, until I arrived, a small bundle of love for both my parents to adore and fuss over. There were many photos of me, lots of my mother holding her treasure, smiling proudly, a few with my father as he liked to take the pictures. It appears that every milestone was collected, captured in an instance to be viewed lovingly over the years and reminisced on.

'You were such an adorable child, Vicki, I never got over the fact that you were given to me. You were a miracle, a wonderful blessing to us. You still are.'

Oh Lord, it must have been really hard for my parents when I left home to start a new life. To be left without their beloved daughter. How strange it must have been, no more tidying up after me, no more conversation around the dining room table in the evenings, no more friends of mine popping in to see me and asking for one of my mum's famous cookies. It was a new beginning for us all. Father, did my mother feel abandoned at that time like your disciples did on that Holy Saturday?

The telephone rings, I hurtle downstairs and pick it up. Unwittingly I recite my home number when a man speaks.

'Sorry I must have got the wrong number.'

'Why?' I ask.

He answers in a hesitant manner.

'Is this or is this not Mrs Green's number?'

I wonder what number I have given. On realising my error I apologise and ask who is calling. The gentleman says he is a Mr Flemming, from Trackwise and would I be interested in a free one month trial offer at their very popular leisure centre? My name or rather my mother's name had been given to him by a Mrs Cowtop, who felt categorically, that I, sorry she, would simply love being a part of a new older ladies group that was being formed to help exercise those areas that do not normally get exercised. That last statement made my mind boggle. I suggested to

171

Mr Flemming that my mother was already getting enough exercise to stimulate the areas that do not normally get exercised. Mr Flemming persisted and I said that the leg waving and arm wrestling was not on her list of to do things before she died. This seemed to do the trick and he courteously said goodbye and hopes that my mother will rethink this offer. So who is Mrs Cowtop?

Oh Lord, our reminiscing was paused for an offer of bigger and better muscles. I think holding an album of memories and turning its pages is more productive than trying to have big guns at this time. Father, our bodies are Your temple, help us, help me not to worship it for its human strength but to allow it to be a vessel for Your power and glory.

I return to my mother's side and ask her who Mrs Cowtop is. She laughs.

'What a daft name, I have never heard of her.' Then she ponders for a moment.

'I wonder if it was Mrs Cruzlop.'

I enquire if she is into older body strengthening.

'Yes,' she says to the degree that Mrs Cruzlop is entering the 'No to Muscle Aging Degeneration' competition for older ladies, M.A.D for short. So that explains the phone call I comment. Then I tell mum that she is being invited to join her friend at the gym for a free month trial. My mother thinks that perhaps Mrs Cruzlop could look after my dad for a free month trial! We both laugh as her statement is rather funny. I am pleased to see that my mum hasn't lost her sense of humour. I look at the time, twelve thirty; it has now been exactly thirteen hours since dad went missing. He must be cold, confused and very lost not to have found his way home yet.

Oh Lord, you are righteous and kind, you are always close to those who call on you. In this hour of need help us, help me to Bless Your Holy name.

I listen for an encouraging word from my Father in Heaven, but there is nothing. He is silent.

Afternoon Prayer

I encourage mum to eat something, as we both need to keep up our strength. It suddenly dawns on me that mum probably hasn't slept since my father went missing. She must be exhausted. I heat up some soup and we both share its contents along with a slice or two of brown bread. Once my mother has finished I suggest that she go upstairs and to rest if possible. I have a feeling that she will just carry on looking at the album so I follow her and ask if I can borrow it. Once my mum is tucked up in bed I slip into Dad's bedroom and follow suit as I am beginning to feel the weariness of the drive up and the emotionally charged events of the day creeping up on me.

Oh Lord, I feel so tired, I am worn out with worry even though I know you are in control of this situation, but I have put my hope in your word and I believe in your promises. I know you will deliver us.

Just as I am about to close my eyes the doorbell rings. I really do not want to answer it, but then again it could be the news we have been awaiting for. I heave myself off the bed and make my way down to see who is calling. Mrs Prost, my mother's next door neighbour, is standing there. She looks strangely at me and then a sudden dawn of recollection appears on her face.

'Vicki, how nice to see you. Is your mother in? I just wanted to tell her that I am sorry about Fred, and that I hope he comes home soon. It is most unlike him to be out so long. Anyway if your mother needs anything just tell her to pop by.'

She disappears without letting me answer and potters off back to her house. Then it strikes me that no one else has rung or called from the neighbourhood to see how my mum is coping with the situation. I find this rather odd and want to ask my mother about this, but I don't want to wake her if she is asleep.

Oh Lord, where are my mother's friends? Her true and faithful friends, those that sing, dance and pray with us even when times are troubled?

Movement upstairs tells me that mum has not managed to settle into a sleep to rest her troubled mind. I brew up a pot of tea and take it up to her. I want to know what has happened to her network of support. I knock and enter her room; she is sitting up in bed and enquires who was at the door. She is surprised that Mrs Prost had come round as they have not really spoken to one another for the best part of six months after Fred had scared her by wielding a garden hoe at her as he attempted to knock out an imaginary mole that was destroying his front lawn. I ask if that is why other people have not called by to see how mum was since dad went missing.

She looks out of the window and replies, 'Yes; a lot of people are scared of his outbursts and strange behaviour. At church one Sunday your father had started to get undressed thinking it was time for bed and shocked the congregation by standing naked and saying his bedtime prayers. He then climbed up on to the altar and lay down on it. There was outrage from all sides; Fred and I were asked to leave. I was mortified, we haven't been back since. No one from the church has contacted me, not even the Vicar since that incident.'

I sigh and say that I wish she had let me know, to which she comments that I have enough on my plate without her troubles.

Oh Lord, you did not turn people away even when they were troubled in mind and spirit. You showed them love and compassion. Father if I see You in real need, help me not to ignore Your suffering, help me not to be afraid and to show compassion and love. If I shy away give me your courage.

The realisation that this has been going on for some time is upsetting to me and knowing that my mother has had to cope with it on her own even more so. Mum had told me obviously that dad was unwell, but I didn't realise that she was trying to cope with his condition on her own.

A thought suddenly occurred to me. 'You have taken dad to the doctor's haven't you?' I say.

She looks at me, shocked.

'Of course I have, love, but getting your father to take tablets when he is having a bad day is really difficult, he has highs and lows and they can happen anytime.'

174

'What about support for you mum? You can't keep going on like this, you need help too.'

'Your dad won't have anyone else in the house, and he certainly won't have anyone trying to do things for him.' She said in an animated fashion.

Mum assures me that she can manage, and she doesn't think anyone else will give dad the care she does. I remind mum that she is seventy five and there is nothing wrong with asking for help. I don't like having a heated discussion with my mother especially in these circumstances.

Oh Lord, we cope, well we try but sometimes things are just beyond us. You know when things are too much for us and You give us signs, nudges, words, and when we still don't get the message you sometimes use a sledge hammer to get through to our stubborn minds. There are times that even this does not work so you use a tornado to shift our cemented attitude. How we must try you at times. Father forgive my stubbornness, my set ways, my inability to change for the better. Grant me the serenity to make the changes you want me to make.

I apologise to my mum, and tell her that I know that she has done everything possible to help my dad. But I know that mum is wondering what is going to happen after this episode. The waiting is horrible and I feel I need to actively do something. I decide to go for a walk, and as I grew up in the area I have a pretty good idea of the places where my dad might have gone. I know that the police have probably already searched the same paths I am going to tread but the thought of actually going out and looking makes me feel like I am doing something to help. I suggest mum comes too but she wants to be home in case there is some news from the police.

Oh Lord, help me find my dad.

I remember playing hide and seek with my dad when I was younger and getting scared when I couldn't find him. I feel a bit like that now. However, he turned up all smiles, his arms outstretched for a hug. I still don't know where his hiding place was to this day. This sense of not knowing where a loved one is brings all sorts of emotions to the surface. The thought that he might have had a fall, collapsed, or been

175

mugged goes through my mind. But surely someone would have found him if that were the case. Maybe he just decided to go for a walk and just carried on. The hypothesizing could go on forever. Somehow I just know he is near.

Oh Lord and Father, how close you are to us, we may not be able to see you but Your presence can be felt if we open our hearts to You.

As I turn the corner into Rosemary Road a particularly favourite street of mine that is covered in cherry blossom in the spring, I notice that the sky looks angry, so angry that it is about to burst. There is a figure approaching me at a pace and just as I am almost in sight of seeing who the person is, the rain clouds dump their full weight of liquid upon me. In one swoop I am soaked to the skin and so is the lady standing opposite me. I don't remember the last time someone smiled so broadly at me in amazement. I gaze at the image of a drowned rat and then slowly my mind places the name of the person who is claiming my attention. Mandy Church, I gasp, and then we hug. I simply can't believe my eyes, my best friend from school, my dearest friend, with whom I had been attached at the hip for ten years. The years have treated her kindly. I try to compose myself but the pain of her parting had been so traumatic that it had never quite been healed. We part and embrace again.

Oh Lord, you know my needs even before I do, how amazing is your timing.

Completely saturated from head to toe, I take my friends hand and lead her to my mother's house. My mother can't quite believe her eyes as she sees my childhood friend. She had loved Mandy as a second daughter and was always thrilled to see her whenever she came to visit, which was frequently back in our school days. Once inside my mother's house Mandy quickly rings her husband to ask for a change of clothing and as we drip and strip out of our drenched attire we finally find our voices. I have so many questions, but first I let Mandy explain her sudden appearance.

'We have just moved into the area and Robert, fed up with unpacking boxes turned the television on and there I saw your father's image. Underneath it was a running commentary on his disappearance, asking for help and information. I just knew that I had to come round to see your mum. I didn't know if she was at the same address, but chances were that she was, as the citation said Fred Green from Blueberry Road.'

Mum gives us towels and we dry ourselves off and moments later Robert arrives with a change of clothing for Mandy. She introduces my mother and me and then he says.

'So you are the infamous Vicki Green.' He gives me a huge smile and shakes my hand.

'Actually I am now Vicki Sponge.'

'Victoria Sponge, how apt, my favourite cake in the world'.

Oh Lord, You are full of surprises, how blessed I am to be the recipient of them.

Mum offers a cup of tea all round, and I can see a glimmer of hope in her eyes again. Mandy and Vicki together again, all that is needed is for dad to turn up now and share in this joy. Mum stops and asks if they have heard about Fred. Mandy replies 'yes' which is why she has come to visit. With tea made we go into the sitting room and we start to catch up on Mandy's life. After the divorce of her parents, Mandy had been taken to Scotland, far away from her alcoholic and abusive mother. There she had been forbidden to write to any of her old friends. Her father was afraid that his ex-wife would try to get an address from Mandy's close school mates. Now I know why she had never written or contacted me. Mandy had struggled with the move and different school system and had dropped out of a promising academic career pathway. She had wandered streets, taken drugs and got into a terrible downward spiral. Then Robert had found her, sick and alone in a hospital bed, when he was visiting his dying mother. Mandy was comforting his mother telling her not to be afraid, that the end was a magnificent release that should not be feared. Robert was struck by this frail young woman who spoke so lovingly to his mother. There was something about her. When his mother died, Mandy asked to go to the funeral; it was the same day as her discharge, and Robert obliged by taking her from the hospital to the church. After the service he had asked her if he could take her home and Mandy told him that she had no home, she had nowhere to go. So he took her in and their friendship grew until they finally got married.

Oh Lord, what a wonderful romance and how beautifully close to Your Love for us. You pick us up when we are down, take care of us and build up our lives again, until we can move on, supported by Your Love. Oh you are such a Glorious God.

Once married, they had longed for children, but unfortunately none came. Then Mandy, coming to the sad realisation that children were not going to be a part of her life, looked for another direction and found her calling. She applied to become a Vicar of Christ. She was accepted and when she saw a position available in this part of the country had applied for it. Mandy was accepted and she and Robert moved down yesterday to take up the post in the church just down the road.

Both mum and I look at each other. 'Not St Andrew's?'

'Yes,' Mandy said.

'What happened to Reverend Steele?' my mother asks.

'He has moved on to greener pastures, I gather there was an incident that he never quite got over.'

'Fred' we both announce at the same time and Mandy looks at both of us. She isn't sure if she should ask for an explanation, but we feel safe enough to share the unpleasant experience with her, as mum is now one of her flock. Mandy takes mum's hands in hers and reassures her that she and Fred are welcome any time into her church. Indeed she would be honoured if they felt they could attend. Oh Mandy, my Mandy, you really are back.

Oh Lord, there are times when you take precious friends away from us, and we do not know why, just like the day you left the tomb and no one could find you. Without them our lives can seem empty, without you our lives are empty. Father help me always to cherish my relationships with those around me and more especially with You. Never let me take my most precious relationship with you for granted.

I think how strange it is that both Mandy and I married a Robert. Then I realise that I do not know Mandy's married name, so I ask.

'Kind' she replies.

Mandy Kind. It suits her. The Reverend Kind. And Mandy was always kind to me. I am so grateful that we have renewed our friendship again and to think it was down to my father's illness that the opening for a new vicar came about and Mandy applied.

God certainly works in strange ways. Robert thanks mum for the tea and says that, although he would rather stay and hear all the wonderful stories he knows we will share, he for one needs to make some head way with the unpacking. Mandy however says that so long as they have a made up bed for the night, everything else can wait. Robert leaves saying farewell and thanks for the cup of tea.

My mum comments that Mandy has arrived in our lives again just at our very moment of need. 'I know Fred will be alright now as we are all together again, this must be a sign,' she decides.

Oh Lord, thank you for your sign of hope, I know that You care and you will bring back Your lost sheep.

With the mood lifted mum starts to think of a cooked meal, she asks what Robert likes as she wants both Mandy and her husband to partake as well. Mandy admits that he is partial to a Shepherd's Pie. My mother's eyes widen, it is her favourite too. No sooner has the decision has been made than my mum starts to prepare the dish. With my mum occupied with the dinner, the telephone rings and I walk into the hall way to answer it, it is the police, just an update to say still no news. The hospitals have been called and they have had no one attend the Accident and Emergency Department bearing Fred's description. There have also been no sightings; it is as if he has disappeared off the face of the earth. This confirms my feelings that he is close by, but not ready to be found yet.

Oh Lord, we are still waiting upon you.

Mandy and I help mum by cutting up carrots and onions. We lay the table in the dining room and I find a candle to put in the middle as a centre piece. All we need now is a bottle of wine. Mandy tells me that a neighbour had popped one round earlier when introducing herself as a 'welcome to the area' present. She would ask Robert to bring it round when the meal is ready. The telephone rings again, this time mum decides to answer it as the shepherd's pie is now cooking in the oven. My mum hands the receiver over to me, it is Lily Pink, she wants to know if granddad has been found and when I am coming home as she misses me. She informs me that something red was put in the whites in the washing machine and her school blouse was now pink. Could she wear it to school as it was a cool colour and went with her name? I tell LP that I won't be back tonight as granddad still hasn't shown up and my mum needs me for a little longer. As for the pink school blouse, no, she could not wear it to school and that she has another two white ones in her wardrobe. Lily Pink wants to push the pink blouse conversation further but I stand firm and ask her to put her dad on the phone after saying lots of 'love you' and ending with kissing noises. The next person on the phone is not Bob though, it is Henry, and could I tell him where his football shirt is as he has a match tomorrow. I suggest that he tries his chest of drawers, and after he has rummaged through them could he put everything back again. He tells me that he has already looked in them, so I suggest that he looks under things rather than just at what is on the top. Gabby takes over then and says that I can take as long as I need at Granny's, as she has everything under control. Bob finally is given the phone and I ask if Johnny is alright. He pauses for a moment, and then says 'yes' but the pause is too long, so I ask again if Johnny is alright. Bob tells me that he is sleeping; that he hasn't been up all day apart from the incident with the broken plate. I reassure Bob that that is normal for a teenager and he will get up when he is good and ready. All he needs to do is make sure that he is fed and watered when he does. I expect he is exhausted from his week at school. Bob asks when I am coming home and I tentatively say tomorrow, all being well if dad has returned by then. My husband tells me to do what is best for my mum and says that they are doing wonders without me. I express my thanks and say that I am glad they are coping alright.

Oh Lord, thank you that my family are trying, things may not be done as I would do them but at least they are attempting to help themselves without the master of the ship guiding them. How dependent we become on our mums and how we miss them when they are not there. I have no idea of how many times you have saved me from myself and my decision making. Only you know of the near misses that I have had trying to do things myself. Father help me to remember that, You are the Master of my ship, without you it would run adrift and crash on the rocks. Thank you that you are a skilled seaman, steering my life through the obstacles that without you, would smash into my world and shred it to pieces. What a wonderful God you are.

I tell mum and Mandy of my conversation and they both enjoy and identify with the red item in the washing! Mandy relates a story that once she had by accident put in one of Roberts red socks, yes red socks, in with her clothes to wash. The next Sunday her parishioners saw her greeting them in a pink tie-dye blouse, which she thought was very fetching but the older ladies felt she was being a bit radical for her office. The image made me laugh. The timer for the Shepherd's Pie goes off and the smell is delicious. Mum grates some cheese on top, puts it under the grill and Mandy rings Robert to invite him to come over and to bring the bottle of wine with him. With all present we sit down and bow our heads, Mandy offers up a prayer of thanks and requests that Fred is found soon, and then we tuck into a most glorious tasting meal. I silently hope that the next meal we have will be in the presence of dad.

Oh Lord, how awesome it is that you are present in everything.

As we eat Mandy asks me about my family and I tell her of the joys and sorrows I have had in having such a varied bag of personalities to raise. It truly has been a blessed task especially with the teenage years that I have struggled with, but have also enjoyed, as my children grow up and develop their God given talents. Mandy and Robert listen attentively, fascinated by my stories and anecdotes. We laugh and cry in hysteria as the world of the Sponges is revealed in all its glory. The revelations of our life make me aware of how complicated my story is at times and that without my faith it would have been unbearable. Mandy identifies with this comment and says that Robert's faith had been her rock in the early days when she was struggling with life and all its complexities. It was later when her own conversion happened that it became evident that only through Jesus was her life complete and worth living. We raise our glasses to God's call to Freedom and sit quietly for a moment to savour the taste of both the wine and our salvation.

Oh Lord, You are the Way, the Truth and the Life; only through you can we find Salvation. You are our Joy, our Deliverer, and our Key to Your Kingdom. Blessed is Your Name.

I await His response, but again there is only silence.

Evening Prayer

Robert thanks mum for the delicious meal, how did she know it was his favourite? He rolls up his sleeves and starts to wash up; it is his act of love for being fed. I really like Robert, there is a natural kindness about him that is rare. He appears gentle and unassuming, but strong at the same time. Mandy certainly fell on her feet when she met him. I ask Mandy what she thinks has happened to my father, and she ponders the question. She has met many people in her life, and counselled countless in her ministry. Her opinion is based on human experience and what she says is important to me. Mandy calmly answers saying that generally if elderly people aren't found early on then they either don't want to be found, or they have been victim to the natural elements of their older life. Alternatively a more heinous conclusion may have occurred, but she didn't feel that that was the case in this situation. Certainly my father's condition has triggered his wandering off, but something must be stopping him from returning or getting help. I tell Mandy of my feeling that he is close by, and she agrees that it certainly is a possibility.

Oh Lord, remember me to the Father, let Him know that I am still waiting.

Mandy, seeing that both mum and I are watching the road outside looking at the passers-by as they meander with their dogs to the local park, knows that we need something to raise our spirits. She asks mum if she still has the guitar that Fred loved to play to us when we were children. I know that I have seen it somewhere in the house, and try to recollect where. Then the light bulb moment happens and I see it in my mind's eye, in mum's room behind the rocking chair. I ask her permission to go and collect it and within moments it is being taken out of its dark blue flimsy plastic case by Robert who is apparently an accomplished player. Mandy suggests that we have a praise party, to thank God for Fred and his life and to celebrate his home coming, trusting that in God's mercy that it will be soon. It seems an odd idea to mum and I but what have we to lose?

Oh Lord, I am your servant, and no matter where I am, so long as I want to be in your presence, you will honour my prayer.

We begin to sing joyous songs, ones that talk of hope and of God's future for us. I feel warmth in my body as I praise my Father in Heaven. Robert stops playing and opens the bible, he reads a passage: "Surely his salvation is near to those who fear him, so our land will be filled with glory. Unfailing love and truth have met together. Righteousness and peace have kissed! Truth springs up from the earth and righteousness smiles down from heaven. Yes the Lord pours down his blessings. Our land will yield its bountiful harvest. Righteousness goes as a herald before him, preparing the way for his steps." (Psalm 85 v 9-13) We sit in silence as we ponder the meaning of these words. An image comes to me of my father standing in the middle of a field with Truth rising from the earth and righteousness smiling down from heaven. He is being engulfed in love as he looks in awe at the magnificence of his surroundings. I sense that he is safe and begin to praise out loud. I don't feel embarrassed by my proclamations, as I am among friends. Now it seems the most natural thing in the world to worship my God for our situation. I am no longer feeling hopeless, but at peace that all will be well. My burden has been lifted by the praise. Mandy sings a beautiful song about God creating the world through his Word, that when he spoke the world began. It appeared at his command. Nothing is impossible for Him who merely says the Word and it is done.

My mother speaks for the first time and she says 'I do', nothing more. As I look at her she has a radiant smile on her face and she looks years younger. I can only imagine that she is receiving from our Father in Heaven. We lapse into silence and allow the time to disappear.

I AM here.

When I hear movement, I open my eyes, it is already ten o'clock. Time has moved on while we were in the presence of God. Mum is sleeping peacefully in her armchair. Robert has a tray of steaming hot tea in his hands. He smiles at me and puts it onto the coffee table. Mandy asks how I am feeling and I tell her that I feel refreshed, light- headed and hopeful. She sits next to me and gives me a hug. We drink our tea and then Mandy and Robert say that if I am alright, they will go home and come back again in the morning. They glance at mum and suggest that I cover her with a duvet and leave her there in her chair as she looks so comfortable. I agree and escort them to the door, we kiss and part, it has been an exceptional day. There is so much to thank God for.

Oh Lord, you came, you saw, you dwelled amongst us, you ministered to our needs. How remarkable you are. I am in awe of your compassion. You have raised my spirits by Your Word.

Night Prayer

Before I retire for the night I seek out a Bible as I want to read of God's promises to his people. I find a well-thumbed edition and take it to bed with me. I open it at random and read and read and read. I cannot put it down. My Father in Heaven has done so many outstanding deeds for us, and our response seems to have been the opposite to his greatest commandment; to love the Lord our God with all our heart, all our soul, and all our mind; his second commandment being equally important, to Love our neighbour as much as we love ourselves. How dismally we have failed. Our answer to the world and its problems are in those two commandments. God has done his ultimate to show us His Love. What is our response? We can only rise if we are obedient to his calling, if we leave our mess at the foot of his cross and walk through the open door of His Love. If we look for him in the open tomb and remain at his last resting place weeping we will not see his risen body, our pains will stay with us, our envy, pride, greed, jealousy, bitterness, anger, and grief will not be wiped clean in God's resurrection. We will remain lost.

Oh Lord, You have given us all the sign posts that we need to acknowledge you as Lord of our life. Help me not to look for the missing Saviour but for the outstanding beauty of the Resurrected Answer.

I am slowly opening my eyes to the purpose of today's 'yes'. I consider that the question has been 'Will you trust and wait for me, will you continue to believe in me during the hours of separation until I am ready to reveal myself?' If I respond in the negative then my world will look very bleak, it will impersonate the desolate barrenness of Calvary after you had died. There is no hope in that place. My 'yes' will mean waiting, having faith, being carried by your Words that you will return.

Oh Lord, YES. I believe. I await your coming.

Now I am ready to sleep, because I know that tomorrow will come and with it a new dawning, because God has spoken and the Word has created a new beginning.

Oh Lord, thank you for an incredible day.

186

Chapter Seven

Sunday

Morning Prayer

'In fact, this is love for God: to keep his commands. And his commands are not burdensome, for everyone born of God overcomes the world. This is the victory that has overcome the world, even our faith.' - John, son of Zebedee; 1 John 5:3-4 (New International Version)

Good morning Vicki.

A jolt awakens me, and something is urging me to get up. My mother is standing over me with a cup of tea. It is seven thirty. She sits on the edge of my bed and says that she wants to go for a walk as soon as I am up and ready. My mum is dressed and has her coat on so I know that this is important to her. As quickly as I can I shower and don my clothing, saying a hello to my Father in Heaven and reiterating my 'yes' for the day. My mum is eager to get going and opens the door to a new day. We walk up the road, looking and listening for anything unusual and then we walk down the road on the other side.

Then almost opposite our house we hear a faint voice.

'Can anybody let me out of here?' coming from the garage of the detached house.

'Hello, anyone there, I really need the toilet?'

The voice is familiar and both mum and I rush to the garage door and try to open it, but our efforts are thwarted as it is locked. Mum calls to Fred and says that he will be out soon. I go to the front door and ring on the door bell, there appears to be no answer. I try again, still no answer, I put my finger on the bell and leave it there; surely this will raise the owners to get out of their bed. Still nothing. I tell mum to continue to reassure dad that he will be out soon and I run back to her house to telephone the police and fire brigade. Each arrives at approximately the same time as well as the ambulance.

187

In no time the garage door has been opened and Fred is set free. He hands one of the policeman several milk bottles filled with yellow liquid.

'Thank goodness you turned up there are no more bottles for me to wee into.'

Oh Lord, and Shepherd, who never tires of looking for your lost sheep, what joy I feel at the return of my father. Praise God.

The paramedic tries to encourage dad to get into the ambulance so that he can check him out, but dad refuses and says again that he needs to go to the toilet. My mum suggests that we escort him home and then once he has made himself comfortable perhaps he will see the professional then. It has been thirty four hours since dad went missing. I take his arm and he looks at me, he searches his memory to find a name, a connection with my face, so I tell him that I am Vicki, his daughter, he shakes his head, still unable to place me. I can see that it is worrying him.

'Vicki, you say, I have a daughter called Victoria, lovely girl.'

'Yes that's me dad.'

'She is so cute, always getting up to mischief with her friend Mandy.' He looks at my mum and asks where Victoria is? I help dad into the house and then return to mum's side. My mother looks at me and has a pained smile on her face. I understand and don't take offence that my dad did not recognise me. He is obviously confused and disorientated by his experience.

Oh Lord, it does not matter that my father cannot place me as his daughter because he is safe and sound back home. Thank you.

The policemen check the garage and find the interior door to the house locked. It appears that the owners are away. He notices a model railway in pristine condition and an armchair next to it. A cool box with its lid removed sits by the armchair and wrappers of various assortments of food have been strewn across the floor. The gentleman had not gone

188

hungry so that was a good thing. As the policemen come out of the garage there seems to be a commotion outside the old gentleman's house.

I see the two policemen leaving the garage; they are unable to secure its door so they leave it ajar for the moment. My dad, having relieved himself has come outside again and is not taking kindly to the ambulance man wanting to do an examination of him in the vehicle. The two police officers now join us trying to convince dad that it would be a good idea to receive some medical attention to confirm that he is alright after his thirty four hour ordeal.

'What ordeal' he says, 'I have spent a perfectly pleasant time mending a model railway, putting books in alphabetical order in the bookcases, reading and eating, I have been well looked after. However I wasn't too sure why I was locked in but I came to no harm. The only complaint I have is that there were no on suite facilities.'

The men all looked at one another. There isn't much they can say to that. My mother calls his name and when he sees her he sees an ally.

'Minnie, tell them I don't need to be examined, I am fine, and I am home. I just want to go to bed. Please Minnie.' He looks at her pleadingly.

'Go inside Fred, I will sort this out'. He obeys and passes me, there is a glimmer of recognition, then his face goes blank again and he shakes his head. I follow him in at a distance.

Oh Lord, in a strange way this is funny, my dad saw his disappearance as a form of holiday. Thank you that no harm came to him and that his abode had been acceptable to him so that he wasn't frightened or felt alone. Father you protected your vulnerable son and allowed his appearance to be known when the time was right. I am so grateful to you my God.

My mother rises to her five feet four inches and talks to the three gentlemen. She tells them that dad has dementia and that any confusion he might have is basically apportioned to this condition. Mum appreciates that they are concerned about her husband but at the

189

moment the best thing for him to do is sleep. Mum invites the policemen and the paramedic into the house in order to fill out the paperwork that is involved when a patient refuses medical assistance from the ambulance service. She signs the declaration that she will be responsible for dad's decision to decline a check-up. Once this has been completed the paramedic leaves saying that if there is any cause for concern on our part then we must either go to the doctors or to the A&E department.

Oh Lord, how often do we decline your help, believing that we can do everything in our own strength? How proud we are, forgive the proudness of man, and forgive my pride.

The policemen are grateful for a cup of tea and when sipping it they report the conclusion of my father's absence to their sergeant. They have one more thing to do before they depart and that is to write a message to the owners of the damaged garage to explain the reason for it. We all muse over the events of the yesterday and its conclusion today, who would have thought that my father was sitting in an armchair fixing a model railway layout while the police were scouring the county looking for my dad. This was going to be one of their more eccentric cases for the archives. One of the men says that we have taken it all very well and he is interested in how we have been so calm.

Mum responds. 'I just knew Fred was alright. After such a long time together, I would have known if anything awful had happened to him. Besides I have God on my side, and he always roots for the weak and fragile. Even though Fred got lost, God provided him with accommodation and had tended his needs.'

The officers looked at one another and said that that was one way of looking at things. They part with sincere wishes that Fred has suffered no setbacks due to his unfortunate incarceration. The policemen pass Mandy and Robert on their way to their car, and they almost race up the pathway wanting to know the latest. I can't wait to tell them our news and they are delighted when I tell them that dad is home again. Mandy says a silent prayer of thanks and we hug and dance about like small children again.

Oh Lord, how great you are, it is in your leaving that we know what it feels like to be separated from your Love. Your return fills us with joy and hope knowing that no matter what, you will carry us through our times of tribulation and strife, and make us stronger if we hand over the situation to you.

My mother having checked up on my father and been happy with his peaceful state announces that we must have a celebratory breakfast. There is a question on my mum's lips.

'Don't you have a service to celebrate as it is Sunday?' Mandy considers the question.

'This is my service today, sharing in your joy. Besides I don't start for another two weeks as I need to settle in first.' We laugh and it is a tremendous release.

As my dad sleeps we tuck into a full English breakfast, blowing our calorie intake for the day and totally unashamed of the medical implications to our coronary arteries. We toast with orange juice and pull crackers left over from Christmas. This is the day that the Lord has made, we rejoice and are glad.

Oh Lord, thank you for being at our table, for sharing in our happiness, for communing with us and making our celebration holy.

As we wash up together I know that I must make the journey back home, and I talk to Mandy about some support for my mother. My friend assures me that she will take matters in hand and encourage my mum to talk about the situation. If anyone can persuade my mother to accept help, I feel certain Mandy will be able to. I take my mum aside and gently tell her that I will have to make my way home. She understands, she always does, but this time she knows things will be different; my leaving will not be as painful, as Mandy and Robert are here. They will visit frequently, and be at the end of a telephone with a quicker response time than I can achieve. Robert offers my mother the use of his laptop, so that she can Skype and feels more connected with the family. My mother looks at him, not knowing quite what he is talking about but grateful for the idea of being more connected. I collect up my things, quietly enter my father's room and kiss him goodbye. He turns over half asleep and smiles at me momentarily.

'Good bye Vicki, nice to see you again.'

It is the fulfilment of my visit, to be recognised by my lovely dad. I could not ask for more. I hug him and he hugs me back.

'Don't forget me love.'

I know I won't, ever, no matter how distant he becomes from reality, I shall never forget who my dad really is and was to me.

Oh Lord our shells may crack and break but underneath this fragile state we are still who you made us to be. We are still your beloved.

I take a deep breath and prepare to leave. I usually find leaving hard, especially as this house has always been the family home. I only ever knew this one abode until I married Bob. I know its every little detail, and yet it is no longer my home. Mandy and Robert have asked mum if they can stay with her for the day to make sure dad is comfortable and mum can relax. I know that she is thankful for their offer and agrees to their kindness. Before I leave I ring Bob to say that I am setting out on my return journey and all has been resolved here to a satisfactory conclusion. He is overjoyed that dad has been found and relieved that I am coming home. Bob wishes me a safe drive and we end our conversation on that note.

Oh Lord, keep me safe on my journey home; help me to look forward as I travel daily towards my encounter with you. May your spirit lead me ever onward accompanying me as I travel homeward.

Sunday morning is a good day to travel and as the sun begins to make its mark on the landscape, hiding then revealing itself through the clouds; I consider the beauty of the countryside. It seems to look different in the revelation of a new day, a day that has seen the resurrection of Hope. My heart feels lighter and I search for a radio channel that has Christian music on it. Together we blast our way to the heavens and back, singing our proclamations of faith. I am so absorbed with the music that I suddenly realise that I am on a part of the motorway that I don't recognise. I have missed my turning! I have no choice but to continue to the next junction and retrace my steps. It seems quite a long way to the following offshoot so I turn the radio down so as not to get carried away again. Finally a junction appears and I am able to make my way back. Funny how easily we can get distracted even when hearing and singing about the wonders of God's love.

Oh Lord, keep me grounded as I am not in your Kingdom yet. There is still the ordinary matter of life's chores to be done as these are part of your work too.

As the familiar road appears again, my heart starts to pound as I think of my family. I try not to think about what is awaiting me in the kitchen and tell myself to trust in Bob's organisational skills, then again, maybe not that skill. I accept that being able to leave them was their gift to me and my mother and anything else will be a bonus. As I drive into our road, there are cars parked everywhere, it seems that families are meeting for lunch by the car load. Fortunately there is just enough room to steer around them into our drive. I look up at the windows of our house, all the curtains are closed and it looks like everyone is still in bed. I unlock the front door and tiptoe in. The house is unusually quiet for a Sunday. I decide that Bob must be up as he answered the phone earlier when I rang, and there is a smell of something, I am not sure if it is from unwashed dishes or if the dinner is already cooking and awaiting my arrival. I enter the kitchen, it is spotless, the oven is on so I take a peek but there is nothing in it. Odd. The dining room door is closed, which is not the norm as it is tends to be left open due to its constant use. I say a tentative hello, no one answers. I say it louder, still it gets no response. Then I hear a giggle, it can only be Lily Pink and a muffled shoosh. I bite my lip as I have stumbled on their little surprise. I open the door quickly and burst in about to say 'caught you', but I am met with a stunning scene. I can only look and gaze at the room. It is adorned with love, the table is decorated and steaming food is sitting welcomingly on the table. My children all clamber to hug me.

'Happy Mother's Day,' they all chant loudly.

What? Mother's Day! A shock thought occurs to me that I have forgotten that it is today and I didn't embrace it with my own mother. My children pick up on my vibes and want to know what the trouble is. I explain what I have just thought about and they ring my mother's number reminding me that the weekend has been full of events that not surprisingly put Mother's Day at the bottom of the pile. My mother answers and I tell her that I have arrived safely and to forgive me for not wishing her a happy Mother's Day. She laughs and says that she doesn't need a day to remind her that I love her. She already knows that. Then she tells me to put the phone down and to enjoy the day with my children.

Oh Lord, how special my mother is and how incredible your earthly mother was. She never waived in her belief in You, no matter what You put her through she embraced it, she followed You to the very end because she knew that You were her Saviour who loved her and that there was no greater love than Yours. Help me to have that same belief, that same courage, to act because I know you are my Saviour.

I turn to my family and sit at the table, the food is getting a little colder, but it still looks and smells wonderful. Everyone talks at once but Bob calls them all to heel and offers a prayer of thanksgiving. We tuck in and share the events of the last twenty four hours. Firstly they all want to know about what happened to granddad, and were stunned to hear that he had only been across the road from us all the time. They had heard me speaking of my childhood friend and were fascinated in her timely arrival on the scene after so many years of being a mystery. By the time I had finished my account we were already diving into a chocolate brownie that Gabby and Lily Pink had made. Now the children took turns to retell their stories.

Oh Lord, retelling the story shows me how your hand was upon the events of the weekend. How long in the planning was your answer, and only when all things were in place were you able to implement your design. What a lesson, Father I am humbled in your greatness, no one else could image your story in its complete form. No one else could have pulled it off so perfectly. All praise and glory to you.

Vicki, nothing is left to chance in my world, nothing is random. I am at the helm always. It is only those that are blind that can't see my weaving in their lives. Everything I do is because I love you.

Afternoon Prayer

Lily Pink starts first as she is jumping up and down wanting to share her time without mummy. She didn't need to tell me about her pink blouse as I already knew about that, but she did need to tell me about the hole in her school jumper that daddy made while trying to iron it. I smile at Bob and he says that it was the only thing he ruined while ironing. Lily Pink continues and tells me about the beautiful card she has made which daddy sat on and managed to ruin. It had stuck to his trousers and now he has a gluey patch on them! She produces her card and in my eyes it is lovely, full of imaginative flowers in a garden fit for royalty. Lily Pink is surprised that I like it and hugs my neck delighted that I can't see the smudges and fibres from Bob's trousers. She gives me a box of chocolates and admits that she has already had a few as she thought I might not be coming home today. I open it and see that there are two left.

'You have saved my favourite,' I exclaim. 'Thank you Lily Pink.'

She blushes at my compliment. 'Oh I tidied my room. Well, dad helped too.' So I congratulate them both.

Oh Lord, thank you for what I have received.

Gabby is next and she tells me that she organised the menu for each day along with a washing up rota. It seemed to be successful as everyone knew what to do, even Bob. Gabby felt very proud of her achievement and I thank her for taking responsibility for the family's welfare. She beams and then produces her card to me. It says 'Thanks for being a wonderful mum' and underneath, Gabby has written, 'I didn't realise how much you do for us without us actually knowing. You are the best!' It is a wonderful accolade from my eldest daughter and a lovely Mother's day blessing from her. Gabby then passes me her present. It is a homemade bracelet with the words, 'I love you' on. I can hardly contain my emotions, it means everything to me.

Oh Lord, to see and hear the words 'I love you' from my daughter makes me feel overjoyed from the bottom of my heart. How incredible it must be then for you to hear our 'I love you' from your children. How the heavens must applaud such

195

expressions of love when it comes from our heart, from the free choice of a broken world, acknowledging you as our God.

Henry decides that he will take his turn now and runs through his weekend. Having gotten off the phone asking me where his football shirt was, he indeed found it, ironed and underneath his favourite top. He had tidied his room, well attempted to do so, as it was rather a tall order to complete it. He now knew where his items were that had been lost for some time. He had found various mouldy bowls and cups that had not helped to perfume his bedroom. Henry had even washed them up as he felt he couldn't ask someone else to do this rancid job as it was his fault the contents had turned to such decay. In fact he had found it fascinating to see what results food neglect could produce. Apparently Johnny had loved exploring the different moulds and had wanted Henry to leave them, but Bob had encouraged his son to dispose of the foul smelling evidence. Henry concluded that his team had won the football match this morning. He then gave me his card, home-made with his face stuck on the front. It said, 'From Your best son to....' And I have to open the card to see the rest of the statement 'Mum. Can you wash my football kit for tomorrow? Love you. Henry.' I have to laugh, who else would use a Mother's Day card to ask a favour like this. Henry's present takes two forms, one a pen and another, a blank book.

'It's for your long awaited reminiscences mum.' Henry has always known that I wanted to write.

I plant a kiss on his cheek and he goes red.

'It's not that great a present mum,' he says, but to me it is inspired.

Oh Lord, my day just got better!

Johnny fidgets on his chair and doesn't say anything. He looks at his desert bowl and finally says that he has nothing to add as he didn't really do anything. The other three dispute this acknowledgement and remind him that he had made them cups of tea when they asked for refreshments. That he had picked up the towels in the bathroom when they were thrown on the floor and he had hovered the front room. Everyone agreed that that was a cracking attempt from him over the weekend. Johnny lifted his head and smiled. His siblings were not going to let him forget how much they appreciated his offerings. Then Johnny hands me a card with a duck on the outside. The words read, 'It's a quacking day for mothers.' Inside it reads 'of all the puddles in the world ours is the best.'

'I made it up mum,' comments Johnny, 'I knew you would find it funny.'

Indeed I do. I hug my son and he winces a bit, trying not to show his fear of being touched. Then he gives me my present. It is a single red rose, my favourite.

Oh Lord, how blessed I am.

With the handing out of the cards and presents over, my children disperse from the table and I am told to go to the living room to put my feet up. I take my cards and presents with me. I hear a lot of clanking of dishes and laughter coming from the kitchen.

'In the bin not over me!' is yelled over an hysterical chuckle.

'Don't you dare Johnny, no!' another shout roars out.

I think I am safer staying where I am. I can't hear the paternal tones of their father so am wondering what he is up to, but that is all; venturing out from my seat would be frowned upon. I decide to turn the television on and to my surprise I recognise the house across the way from my mother's. The reporter on the national news is saying that this garage is where a seventy eight year old man had been locked up since late Friday night. As the occupants of the house are not home to comment it is not known how Mr Green was imprisoned there. A search is now on for the owners of the house.

Oh Lord, how twisted the media can make things, an innocent action leading to a major investigation. A local event becoming nationwide. I am sure that there is a simple explanation, but someone wants a bigger juicier story. Father help me not to blow things out of proportion, to be realistic in my expectations of life.

I turn the TV off and shake my head. The Green's make headlines but for the wrong reasons! As I look at the assortment of cards, all made by hand and with careful thought, I cannot dampen the joy I feel at being a mother. The presents too, chosen because my children know that I love chocolate, bracelets, flowers and expressing myself. How well they know me. In time the children join me, along with Bob and a welcome cup of tea. He is holding the carrier bag from Munday's.

'I bought you this as I thought you deserved it.'

I unwrap the object from its tissue paper and find a new mug; it says 'A mother is not just there to pick up the pieces, but for life.' It is quite apt and I have to chuckle. 'Precisely,' I conclude.

Oh Lord, you are not just here to pick up our pieces; you are here to redeem us, to give us another option in our fraught lives and to set us free, to set me free. Alleluia.

My children ask me what I would like to do this afternoon and I consider their question. The sun is shining outside, and it looks like a glorious excuse to go for a walk. I am feeling quite tired, but a trip to our local beach comes to mind. It is welcomed by one and all and Bob gets the key to the car. I put an extra sock over my foot to prevent the sand from rubbing on my poorly toe and realise that I have not noticed any pain recently. Then everyone clambers in the car and we head for our favourite golden sands. It doesn't take long and although there is a cold chill in the air even with the sun shining its hardest, the scene is breath taking. I have always loved the sea side. There is something sensational about the vast expanse of water and the way it ends up lapping onto the sand. As I touch the end of its run before it disperses again and rolls backwards and forwards, I think about my life. How often have I touched the ocean wanting to take the plunge into its unfathomable depths to discover its secrets, but often shy away, frightened by its enormity. Have I refused to dive into unknown waters and missed opportunities because I am afraid? Have I sat back because my courage has failed me? If so then it is time to change that through the experience of the Resurrection. I must place my self made crosses into the light of the resurrection and allow God to heal them. If I don't then the Spirit of this World will use these weapons of self-destruction against me in a bid to stop me from fully receiving God's healing in my life. I have a choice; hang on to the nails that bind me to these self made crosses or to be transformed by God's victory. Help me to choose your Victory.

Oh Lord, I am bound by my human draw backs, your cross is enough for me, help me not to take or accept anything other than your challenges in my life. If I am blighted by anything that hinders my journey to you, uproot it and take away those thorns that burden my life. Expel the thoughts that tell me that I am not worthy, the actions that say I am not capable, and the deeds that I do in my own strength and for my gratification. Help me to do all things in Your Name and for Your Name, giving you the Glory and Honour that you deserve.

When I look around I see Bob and the kids working together to make a substantial sand castle. Only Johnny is standing on his own looking out to sea. I go and tuck my arm into his.

'Life is like the sea, one moment calm and uneventful, the next raging with a force destined to drown you,' he gently expounds.

'Johnny, life is what we make of it. It is frightening for all of us, no one knows what it has in store for us, but always remember that there is a life boat ready to rescue us when we think we are about to drown.'

Johnny nods thoughtfully.

'Besides, you want to become a scientist; that is something to look forward to, a life of discovery.'

Johnny brightens up, 'Yes, scores of interesting facts to learn and microscopes to look down. Our Earth is awesome mum, it holds so many mysteries and I have a life time to unravel as many as I can.'

'That's my young man, keep exploring. Because once you find one answer it will lead to another question. You have no end of material to keep you busy for as long as you live.'

This proclamation seems to thrill my son, his thirst for knowledge will be forever challenged, as only God knows all the answers and man is nowhere near the tip of exploring all of them. Like an iceberg we see just a little bit above the sea line but never the entire structure that is beneath the surface.

Oh Lord, what a powerful analogy that is. Indeed we only see a snippet of your power, and when we do we wonder at its capability, but it is nothing to the extent of what you can do. We would be totally blown away if we saw your true energy source.

Having harvested the energy from the sea, I go and join in with making the sand castle. It is simply amazing. It has turrets, a moat, an outer and inner sanctum, the impression of a portcullis, a keep and a princess called Lily Pink, who dances around the castle showering everyone in sand swept up by her movements. Then disaster, a dog chasing after a ball along the beach hurtles straight through our creation.

Henry shouts 'Attack, attack, we are under attack.'

Everyone rises and tickles each other until we are gasping for air. The owner of the dog finally catches up with his pet who is yapping at our heels as we collapse onto the ruined fortress. He apologises and sees that no harm has been done. Sand is everywhere, down my coat, inside my blouse, attached to my hair, but who cares; we have had a fabulous time together, another memory for our scrap book of reminiscences.

Oh Lord, your Bible is full of reminiscences, full of your deeds for your chosen people. But your Words are just as relevant today as they were when they were written, because your love affair with your people will never end and each generation is as important to you as the next. Love the Lord Your God, crosses all ages, all languages, all religions. It is exactly what it says it is, Love the Lord Your God, no 'if' he exists, no 'but' he might exist, no 'just' in case he exists, simply Love the Lord Your God because He does. His Word says He does and who am I to disagree?

We all shake off the excess sand from our clothing, closing our eyes as one or other of the family brushes any remaining fragments away. I turn to look at the sea again, I didn't actually go for my walk but the outing has been a great success none-the-less. When we get back to the car we take off our shoes and bang them together to get rid of the grains that have seeped into our footwear. Socks are stripped off and thrown into a bag in the boot. With spirits high we head back home,

200

everyone talking over one another about their antics on the beach. I listen with closed eyes; the fresh air has made me feel exhilarated but at the same time fatigued. All I want now is a shower to wash away the last of the sand and to refresh my weary body.

'Bags a shower first' I lay my claim. Then I look at Bob and ask if there is any hot water.

'Hopefully' he says, through the side of his mouth. Back home the bathroom is left for me and thankfully there is hot steaming rejuvenating water as I step into the shower. Bliss. My bandage on my toe comes off and will need to be replaced, but the water is soothing on its swollen mass.

Oh Lord, nothing does it like a shower, the feeling of gushing water flowing over my head, cleansing my body and making me feel fresh again. I am renewed.

You are indeed renewed my daughter.

Evening Prayer

After my shower the bathroom is a free for all. Lily Pink and Gabby decide to share and from the screams and shouts are having a whale of a time. Johnny goes next then Henry and last of all Bob. He has pulled the short straw as there are no dry towels or hot water left. He jumps in and out very quickly. Everyone is ravenous, but they refuse to let me do anything. Johnny does some sandwiches that look like door stops, so I only need a half slice; he looks hurt, so I take another one, with the intention of giving it to Bob when he puts in an appearance. There is a giant slab of cake for afters, again I try to take the smallest but even that is huge. I feel very spoilt and very happy.

Oh Lord, how the heavenly throng must have felt when you entered the Kingdom of Heaven. What music and dance would have filled the vast City? What a magnificent scene that must have been. You the Resurrected King, home forever. But in all the celebrations that have erupted ever since, you have never forgotten us who are still on the Earth. We are still in Your Mind and Heart, a heart burning for us to join you. Father, may I always have a burning desire to be with you eternally.

Before the evening performance that has been practiced for me during the weekend, I announce that I want to ring my mother again. Once on the phone mum tells me about the neighbours coming home and finding the garage door open. Robert went over to tell them about the saga of the weekend of which they were completely unaware, as they had gone out of the country. Mr Dobson, the owner, was horrified that he had locked my father in his garage. Apparently he had briefly gone out to put something into it, forgotten to shut it properly, and when later checked it before they left, had locked it totally unaware that my father had wandered into it. Hearing that they were being looked for by the media to explain why they had imprisoned a vulnerable old age pensioner, Mr Dobson contacted the police to clear up the matter. I ask how dad is and mum says that he hasn't stirred a lot from his bed. Mandy and Robert have gone home and reassured mum to ring them anytime if she needed anything. Mum said that she was tired and was planning on going to bed early. I think that that is a good idea and wish her a peaceful night.

Oh Lord, bring wholeness and peace to my mum as she rests in sleep tonight.

The show is about to begin. Lily Pink is dressed in a yellow tutu brandishing a wand. She tries to make Johnny appear, but he isn't sure if it is scientifically correct to do so.

'Just think of Doctor Who,' Henry encourages.

This seems to help and Johnny appears from behind a blanket.

'Who do you think I am?' he questions.

'Um, Doctor Who?' I announce.

'Mum, you are not supposed to say anything,' Lily Pink reprimands me.

Henry is laughing; he seems to think it funny. The play has everything in it, fairies, pirates, a gymnast, a one eyed frog, a cowboy, spaceman, a dead cow, not forgetting Doctor Who. When it ends I can't stop clapping, because it is brilliant. My sides hurt from laughing so much. Bob has recorded it and we decide to watch it over again on the TV so that the children can see their production. Just before we start, Holly and Ken knock on the door asking for news of my dad. We greet and hug and I tell them that all is safe and sound now at my parent's house. I invite them to sit and watch the kid's movie. It is hilarious once again, and I feel so proud of them. Holly and Ken are crying with laughter, on the settee with Bob. There are prompts every so often as someone says that the lines were wrong or forgotten, but the improvisation was even better. I am not sure why there was a dead cow, but it didn't seem to matter. Johnny enjoyed playing it and that was good enough for me. Bob sorts out drinks all round as everyone is thirsty. I insist that there is a bow by the actors and an encore. The dead cow puts in an appearance again and Lily Pink does a cartwheel over it. Then she snuggles into me and we have a long cuddle.

Oh Lord, what a great way to end a day. These, your children, have excelled themselves in serving me and in dishing up a spectacular performance. They were not hindered in showing me their skills and love; they just wanted to please me. Thank you that their love has been so generous today. Father, your son's rising showed your boundless Love for us, help me to always be mindful of your sacrifice for me and its ultimate reward.

203

We are all on a high, with energy bouncing off the walls. But there is the boring matter of school tomorrow. Lily Pink asks if I can read her a story before bedtime, and the others decide that I haven't read them one in ages too, so they all sit down to listen. I choose a story about how much a mother loves her children. By the time I finish her arms are outstretched, open to all the orphans in her home town. Her children were all the waifs and strays of a world that didn't care about the poor and weak, whose throwaway motto included those that were handicapped and diseased. There is silence, Lily Pink asks if that was just a story, and I say unfortunately 'no', it is a real story and it still happens today. She wonders why I have told them such a sad story, and I respond with how lucky I am to have such a loving family, to be able to celebrate Mother's Day with my children who are adored and were always wanted. I continue, in our happiness we can often forget the forgotten of our world, the unseen, the unloved. I remind my fortunate bunch that there are children with no mothers or fathers to love them, and therefore we have a duty to remember them so that they are not forgotten. Johnny asks if he would have been an unforgotten if I hadn't been his mum and he had been abandoned. I look at him and shake my head.

'No one would forget you, not after that performance of Doctor Who and the dead cow!' They all laugh and ruffle his hair.

Bob makes a comment, 'Always treasure your mum.'

Each come and gives me a hug and a kiss and I give them a big thank you for a lovely day. The children also offer Holly and Ken one with Bob pointing to his cheek expecting the same attention.

Before they nip off upstairs, I point out that they should always treasure their dad too.

Oh Lord, you treasure everyone. Thank you.

Holly and Ken don't stay for much longer as they can see that I am beginning to fade. But they appreciate being invited in to see the amateur dramatics. Once our friends leave, Bob and I go upstairs, he to read and I to just rest on the bed and if sleep comes then so be it. As I lie on my back I think over the events of the day, it has been extraordinary. In fact the last two days have been a real test of our faith. Were we found wanting, did we allow thoughts of desertion to take over our minds? If we did I am sure God was merciful.

Oh Lord, I take consolation in the fact that your disciples on the road to Emmaus doubted, and when you accompanied them they told you that they had hoped that the prophet who died on the cross was the Messiah. You called them foolish people, your own disciples. You had to explain everything over to them again, referring to God's Word. But it was not until you broke bread with them that their eyes were opened and they saw you. Father how many times have I doubted you, have I looked away not seeing you? Forgive my lack of recognition and keep me close to Your Word that speaks only of the Truth.

Today is Sunday, the day of the Resurrection; my week has culminated in today's revelation.

Vicki, how brave you have been to walk with me during this Holy Week. You have freely said 'Yes' to each new day never knowing what would cross your path. Thank you for your faith.

My dear daughter, always remember that your value is not in what you do, but with who made you. Your recipe is complete and now you can go forward with My book of ingredients to make an even more beautiful witness to My baking.

I don't think that I am any different, I check my face in the mirror but it is still the same as it was when I looked at it this morning. I am still Victoria Sponge. But something tells me that I am different. I sense a feeling of awareness, of not being afraid to speak about God. I feel more courageous, able to proclaim the Holy Week message.

Oh Lord, help me to continue my journey towards Your resurrection and even when there are days when it seems I am back on the road to Calvary again remind me to seek your Face to renew my Hope in Your Faithful Word.

My Evening Prayer is melting into my Night Prayer as I drift in and out of sleep.

Are you ready for the next challenge my love?

I am if you are going to walk with me Lord.

Do you love me Vicki?

Yes Lord, you know I love you.

Then feed my children.

Do you love me Vicki?

Yes Lord, You know I love you.

Then take care of all those who turn to you for help.

Do you love me Vicki?

Yes Lord, you know everything; you know that I love you.

Then feed, care and lead all those who come to you for nourishment to ME, to My Word. I am not asking you to do this in your own power, but in the Power of the Holy Spirit.

I bow my head in the light of this commission and turn the light off to another day. My life will no longer be the same.

How I delight in you Victoria Sponge. Good night my love.

As the day draws to a close and the moon shines in the sky overseeing the sleeping and the restless, Victoria Sponge rises.

How to make Victoria Sponge Special

Take One Baker

Gather Soul ingredient

Read the Word

Mix with Heart

Add Spirit

Bake and allow to Rise

Epilogue

So what now Lord? Our Holy Week journey has come to an end.

Now is only the beginning Vicki. I wanted you to see how relevant my story and yours is. How much they are intertwined. How your day can be a prayer no matter what is going on.

You do not have to do marvellous and daring things to be like Me. Your daily offering of 'Yes to God, no matter what' is like a beautiful fragrance. In the old testament my people offered up sacrifices to me, today I do not want sacrifices but an open heart with a will to say 'Yes'. Your very presence because it is willing to be in my company is acceptable to Me.

Is that all you want Father, my presence?

Do you know what you are saying Vicki? All your presence is an enormous present to me, that you know me, see me, hear me, read of me, eat of me, drink of me, follow me, praise me, worship me, speak of me, share your time with me and love me. When you do all of these You are proclaiming my Kingdom come, and joining in the prayer that I gave you to say: Our Father who is in Heaven, hallowed be Your name, Your Kingdom come, Your Will be done, on earth as it is in Heaven, give us this day our daily bread and forgive us our trespasses as we forgive those that trespass against us and lead us not into temptation, but deliver us from all that is evil. For God's is the Kingdom, the Power and the Glory.

When you say it like that Father, I can see that by including you in all that we do, we are part of Your Universe, Your Creation, and Your Love, my constant companion on my journey through life.

Vicki, you are a Jewel from my Father's Crown. Shall we continue?

208

Yes, Lord.

Then take my hand and follow me.

Just one thing more Lord. Is my life going to change from now on?

Vicki, you will still have your trials because you live in a fallen world. There will still be things that upset and annoy you. There will still be injustices in your life and others, but what will have changed is the fact that you have Hope and the Holy Spirit to guide you along the journey.

I will continue to be your greatest friend, never engaged or distracted, always available to listen, to heal, to love. All things will still be in my time and for your very best intentions.

Remember in my presence you will always find Peace and Light, and if you are troubled seek out my Word.

Lay your life upon me and I will give you Rest.

No other God can promise this, because when the Word was spoken, all creation came into being, and everything comes from the Word.

A Jewel in the Sponge

(Johnny' Story)

"All the world's problems started when one man

believed something that wasn't true.

And most of your problems start the same way.

Who are you listening to?"

(Ray Watson www.secretplaceministries.org)

Chapter One

The Call

Tuesday evening - (as taken from the book 'How to make Victoria Sponge Chapter Two)

'I hate you mum. I hate myself. I hate my life. I hate God.' Johnny forcefully says at the top of his sobs. 'I want to end it all. I have had enough. I know how to kill myself. It would be better for all of us if I were not alive. I am too much trouble, a nuisance and I would be better off dead.'

Wednesday evening – (as taken from the book 'How to make Victoria Sponge Chapter Three)

'Dear Mum

I am sorry for the things I said to you. I don't hate you mum, I just get so angry inside with myself for being me. I don't understand who I am, but thank you for your love, for knowing my limitations and accepting them.

I feel like I am serving a life term in prison. I see you standing out of reach; I try to reach you but my body and mind are trapped behind the bars. I stretch my arms as far as possible but the bars prevent me from reaching you, from hugging you showing my true feelings. I am a prisoner unable to escape the cell of my disability.

I long to be free to express my inner self, to be part of your world, to join in and be like everyone else. I hate being different, trapped in a parallel world. A world alien to you and the family. Seeing, unable to partake. There is no key, not even a lock to put a key into, no release.

I am a reluctant prisoner, confined indefinitely, with no reprieve date. What heinous crime have I committed to be serving this sentence? How do I find freedom?

I may not show it but I do love you, I always have.

Thanks for hanging in there for me.

Johnny.'

Wednesday night. As all the Sponge family are asleep. Vicki and Bob, Johnny's parents, Henry, the eldest son, Gabby, Johnny's twin, and Lily Pink the youngest of the brood snore at different levels as a light manifests itself in Johnny's room.

Johnny.

'Who's there?' a dishevelled teenager asks sleepily.

Johnny.

'What? I am trying to sleep!' He says getting annoyed.

Johnny.

'Give it a break, will you!' Johnny utters and pulls the duvet over his head.

I have come in answer to your prayer.

Johnny slowly raises the duvet and peers out from under it. 'You have come in answer to my prayer? Are you having a laugh?'

No Johnny, I am deadly serious, you called, and in fact you implored my help.

'What? When? I never called you. Who are you?'

Do not be afraid Johnny.

'Hang on; you come into my bedroom in the middle of the night. I don't know who you are and you tell me not to be afraid. Um, so who are you exactly?'

Do you remember your words yesterday when you were upset and miserable? You told your mother you hated her and you said that you hated God too?

'But I apologised to my mum, she understands. If I apologised to my mum and that is okay… oh my goodness… are you from above, have you come to take me away? I'm sorry, I am really sorry, I didn't mean to say I hate anyone, honestly, I….'

I love you Johnny. I know that you don't hate me, and I want to show you how much I love you.

'Right now, in the middle of the night?'

There is no night or day where we are going Johnny, just light.

'So you want me to go with you, a stranger, to who knows where? Doesn't that sound a bit odd to you?'

Trust me.

A hand stretches out to Johnny, a hand that is torn with the scars of a nail having being driven through it.

You know who I am Johnny.

Johnny gasps, 'My Lord and my God.'

Chapter Two

The Doors

Johnny takes hold of his Guide's hand and steps into a Spiritual World. There before him stand seven doors, each on its own without any support. Each bearing a colour with a door handle on it. Red, orange, yellow, green, blue, indigo and violet.

Johnny, I know your pain and I want to show you how precious your life is. Each door you step through will show you the meaning of your life and why I love you so much. Why I don't want you to take your own life, to feel worthless, and alone. I made you for a reason. Step forward now and open the first door.

'What, on my own Lord?'

No my son, I will be with you, I am always with you. Remember that Johnny, I am always with you.

Johnny reaches for the first door, the red door and opens it.

Chapter Three

Red

'Adam it is so beautiful here,' Eve states enthusiastically. 'I love this garden, the colours, the vegetation, the animals, the warmth, our love. It is exquisite. God is such an amazing Creator.'

'Sit Eve and settle beside me,' Adam smiles and holds out his hand to her. She obliges and in their nakedness they know no sin.

See how innocent my first creation is Johnny, unblemished and beautiful. My prize, the two people, sitting in love, gazing at the spectacular scenery I have made for them, their eyes smitten with My Work and each other. It is an amazing mosaic.

'Are these two people Adam and Eve from the Bible Lord?'

Yes Johnny they are.

'Then this is before the Fall?'

Quite right my son.

'Why would they want to leave all of this? It is truly breath-taking, my Lord.'

Indeed it is. But having a creation that just is, is no different from having made the lion or the lamb sitting down together in a happy union.

'So you wanted something different from your first humans.'

Yes I wanted them to choose, to have free will, to want to be with me and my creation, not just be there because it is comfortable and because they know no different.'

'Is that why they were tempted?'

I gave permission for them to be tested. Adam knew the rules as I had explained them to him before Eve was created.' (See Genesis 2:16-17) **'I made it abundantly clear to Adam that if he ate of that particular tree he would surely die.**

'So Eve wasn't there for that conversation?'

No she wasn't, and because of that she listened to a lie, she listened to something that was close to the truth, but not the exact truth that came from my lips.

'So why didn't Adam stand up and say that what the serpent said was false?'

Because the serpent put doubt into Adam's mind through Eve. Adam avoided responsibility; he should have stood up for his wife and silenced the doubts with the words of Truth, the Words I had given him.

'The Fall comes from a lie then.'

Yes Johnny, a lie.

'Is my life a lie Lord?'

No Johnny, your life is not a lie. But things have happened to you to make you believe the lies that have been spoken over you. Let's look at one of the events that have been triggered by those lies.

The scene changes to Johnny's school. There in the playground a group of boys are laughing and taunting another student.

Do you recognise the young man, Johnny?

'Yes, it is me'. Johnny looks uncomfortably at the image; a hand rests on his shoulder as he watches the scene.

'I hate those boys for what they have done to me.'

Hate or distrust?

'What do you mean?'

Hate is a very deep and powerful word. Hate has led to innocent nations almost being exterminated. Distrust on the other hand, means that you doubt the actions and sentiments of what the person is saying and doing. That they are lying to you in some way or other.

'Alright, so I distrust these students. They spoke lies over me and made me look weak and vulnerable. They took away my dignity and laughed at my differences. No, I do hate them. They murdered my character and thought I was disposable, a piece of rubbish to be kicked about.'

I understand your anger Johnny, what they did was wrong, as they followed the serpent in his ways. But I love them too, Johnny, as much as I love you.

'Really? How? Why? They are in the wrong, they hurt me!'

Did I stop loving Adam and Eve because they were disobedient, because they listened to the serpent? Who did I come to save, to redeem? Everyone Johnny, every sinner on the earth. Do I hate my enemies? I died so that they could have a new life, eternal life. I forgave, can you?

'What you are asking is a tall order, Lord, I am not sure I can do it.'

With the help of my Father's Spirit, all things are possible Johnny.

'Then Lord, with the Father's Spirit, I will try.'

You are a brave young man, Johnny.

'I don't feel brave Lord.'

219

Let us look at another example.

Another image appears. Johnny is sitting in a classroom with his Head of Year, his dad and his mum. He is being questioned about who the bullies are who have been causing Johnny so much distress. He names the main perpetrator. The Head of Year's own son.

You say you are not brave Johnny, but you looked deep within yourself to find the courage to name the leader of the troublemakers, even though you know you will not be believed by the man who is questioning you. That takes courage, a lot of courage. You stood up for yourself.

'I suppose.'

There is no suppose, you did. You started the journey to reinstating your value. And I am here to show you that your value comes from Me, not from the lads who abused you. That is the Truth.

'My worth, my value comes from You, that makes better sense. From my Creator and not from the mouths of bullies. If Adam and Eve had believed that, they would still be in the Garden of Eden. They chose to believe that they could become like You, God like, knowing everything. They put their value in gaining knowledge'. (See Genesis 3 v 4).

Adam and Eve did not need to gain more knowledge, as they had Me, but the serpent promised them greater knowledge. How much greater can you get than God?

'Their logic was flawed.'

Yes because it was based on a lie. Your tormentors thought they would get a buzz out of demeaning you, would gain status because they got away with it, but they didn't count on your strength, you revealing them, on bringing their lies to the surface. You outsmarted them. Adam was afraid, he chose to do something that he knew was wrong, he should have led Eve away but instead he was submissive and followed his wife in the sin.

The students did the same. They knew what they were doing was wrong but they didn't walk away either, so both examples have been turned out of the familiar into the unknown, where they will have to make a new beginning.

'Does this not sadden you Lord?'

I am not saddened by man's existence but by the fact that man follows the sin. I will always be there for him, indeed Salvation has already been won for my creation. Adam and Eve left the Garden of Eden with free will, I am big enough to embrace that. Indeed I have been embracing it ever since.

'But you did get quite angry at one point Lord.'

Yes, and I had to use an image from above My throne to remind myself not to end mankind's existence. (See Rev 4 v 1-3)

'The rainbow?'

Yes, the rainbow that signifies the beginning and the end, Genesis to Revelations, each colour is part of the production of light. All the colours together make light, white. This colourful reminder is of mercy, forgiveness and love, making all things new again, washing them clean, the promise of Salvation for all.

'So we came through a red door, what was the significance in that?'

Red is the first colour of the rainbow. Adam was made from red clay/earth; he was the first man, the beginning of mankind. He also was a participant in the first sin and listened to the first lie. Without the first Adam there would be no second Adam and no redemption.

'So even though Adam and Eve messed it up right from the beginning, you still loved them.'

Yes, that is about the size of it.

'Wow, you are cool!'

Yes I am one cool God who loves Johnny Sponge.

'That's awesome.'

But Adam and Eve weren't the only ones to mess up. The Bible is riddled with sinners. You can get lost in the maze of human hodgepodge.

'Like who?'

There's Jonah, Jacob, Moses, David, Peter and Paul, to name but a few.

'And you still loved them?'

Yes Johnny, every one of them and their messing up still accomplished good things in spite of their limitations.

'I am limited Lord.'

You are limited for a reason Johnny, and not the one you think you are limited by. I have chosen you to achieve great things because of your limitations. I want to use your life for my honour and glory, just as I did with all the people I have chosen before you.

'But I am trapped in my mind, in my understanding of life and people. I don't understand how the world works.'

That is why you are perfect Johnny; you are a perfect choice for my calling.

'I still don't understand Lord.'

Your mind, Johnny, is free from the complications of the world; you have a unique take on what is happening around you. Everything you do isn't marred by the spoils of normality. As you

222

overcome your challenges man will know that the power of change has come from Me and me alone. I will be your key.

'You read my letter to mum?'

I know everything Johnny, whether it is written or not. I did not need to see your letter. I AM your Freedom.

Johnny looked at God and began to cry. The tears flowing were not for sadness but for joy, for release, for acceptance.

Do you feel more able now to forgive the boys who hurt you, knowing that I have forgiven mankind their misdoings?

'Yes Father.'

Take this red ribbon as a reminder of this moment.

As Johnny is only wearing his pyjamas, he ties the ribbon on to one of his button holes.

We need to move on now Johnny as the red door has revealed its secret to you.

Johnny takes one last look at the Garden of Eden, its beauty and innocence. The beginning of all, before the Fall.

Chapter Four

Orange

Back in the main room Johnny sees that the Red door has closed and its light has grown dim from around the edges of its frame. He looks towards the next door, aglow with brilliance, bursting to be opened, its rays filtering through the cracks encouraging Johnny to step forward and seek its meaning.

Are you ready Johnny, for the next door?

'Yes Lord, I am ready.'

The light behind the Orange door comes from a single fruit that is lying on a white table standing alone in the middle of a large room. Johnny partly shields his eyes in order to become accustomed to the glare. He turns and says in a confused manner,

'What has an orange got to do with anything?'

What does orange symbolise Johnny?

'The fruit or the colour?'

Both.

'The colour makes me think of fire, joy, warmth, the setting sun, changing seasons, it's a bright colour; not one I would choose to wear as it makes you visible. It makes me uncomfortable. The fruit, well I suppose it encourages you to eat it as it is a warm colour, one that you can trust. However you have to peel it and that can be hard at times when the skin is taut. Sometimes I have to get my teeth into it first to start the process of peeling. It is a helpful fruit as it already comes in segments to be broken off and eaten individually.'

Beautifully put Johnny, you have a wonderful grasp of language

224

and of using your knowledge to make an object come to life.

'I do?'

You do!

'But normally I can't speak this way, it gets muddled and I feel tongue tied especially in front of other people. I don't like being the centre of attention; it is scary, especially when everyone looks at me.'

I know Johnny, but look how capable you were just now in describing orange. You came alive, your eyes lit up, you took on a different form.

'I did?'

You did!

'Wow that has never happened before.'

You have never entered the Orange room before.

'So what is the Orange room about Lord?'

One of the descriptions you used was the changing of the seasons. Remember that before the Fall there was no sin, but after the Fall there was. The work of man became hard, he toiled for little gain, but toil he did to feed and fend for his family. But if a man toils for his own gain and does not believe in Me then it is all for nothing. Like autumn leaves man will wither and die when his deeds are dead. (See Isaiah 64 v 6)

'I don't understand Lord what you mean by his deeds being dead?'

Johnny, the bullies, their deeds were sinful, they came from a sinful nature (see 1 Corinthians 3 v 3) **for anyone who builds on a foundation of sin will be tested by fire, and die like the autumn leaves do. Their deeds were not based on My work, but spoiled by the prince of this world.** (See 1 Corinthians 3 v 10-15)

225

'So whatever we do, we must do for love of you, not for ourselves?'

That is right Johnny, because those that know Me, show it by their love and actions which are centred in My Love. The changing of the seasons symbolises a person changing from self-made love to God-made love that is inspired by the Holy Spirit. So whatever you do in My love with the guidance of the Holy Spirit will be fruitful and uplifting to those that receive from you.

'So bad deeds are dead deeds?'

Yes, but dead deeds can be deeds done by Christians who do them in their own strength too. For example, if someone cleans the church, helps with Children's Liturgy, does the coffee after a service and constantly wants praise for all their efforts then they are doing it for the wrong reason, and nothing is reaped from those deeds as they are done for their own glory. Their reward is in the praise they receive from man. So in all things seek to do them for my honour and glory in the quietness of your heart and the silence of acclaim.

'Even school work?'

Even school work, because you are using your talents to honour Me when you gain knowledge to further your gifts.

'But if I am successful in my exams?'

If you are successful in your exams, shout for joy, because you are honouring me and the effort you have put into achieving your goals that I have called you to accomplish. In your efforts your life will be changed, because you have tried and called on my name first. This is how you reap the rewards of your daily performance in my sight.

'So the Orange room is about changing?'

The Orange room is about change, but it is also about healing, as you pass from one season to another, being prepared to move on.

This can only happen if you have forgiven yourself and others the grievances that have shaped your life. Remember the orange fruit, how you have to peel its skin off before you can eat it? Some skins are tougher than others due to hurts from the past. If you are prepared to allow me to peel the skin away and take each segment of your life and heal it, then the seeds can be replanted by my Holy Spirit. Each segment makes a whole and if one is damaged then it will affect the whole fruit. By My wounds you will be healed Johnny. I am the healer of broken hearts, (See Ps 147 v 3) I want to heal you Johnny.

'Father, I want to be healed.'

Then never let the sun set on a hurt, no matter if it is a cruel word spoken over you or an action that betrays you and causes you grief. Before the night is out place all those burdens at the foot of my cross where they can be drenched in my precious blood and healed.

'Father that is hard to do.'

I know Johnny, but remember I did it first. And I did it because I love you.

'Yes Father.'

Johnny what other words did you use to describe orange?

'Fire, joy, warmth.'

Exactly my son, fire for the passion I love you with, joy for the emotion I feel for you and warmth for the hugs I long to embrace you with when you turn to me. Johnny may all your deeds be orange.

Johnny looks around for the exit door but it is no longer there.

'Father, how do we leave this room?'

227

There is an escape hatch in the floor, but only you can find it.

Johnny looks around the room but does not see anything. He paces its full width and length but again finds nothing.

Sometimes Johnny the answer is hidden within the question.

Suddenly it dawns on Johnny to move the table with the orange on. There underneath is a trap door. He leans over and touches the handle but it is red hot to touch. Johnny moves his hand away very quickly and looks at God.

'I can't open it Father.'

You will never be given anything that you can't handle Johnny. Remember who you are and why you are here.

'I am Johnny Sponge and God loves me, I am … what Father, what am I?'

My beloved son, strong and vulnerable, great and special, courageous and kind.

'I am Johnny Sponge.'

Try the door handle again.

Johnny stoops to touch the handle, it is cold as ice, and freely comes away as he pulls it open. Below he sees a multitude of colour of oranges, from bright red with a glint of orange, to bright amber with a hint of yellow. Johnny looks at his saviour who encourages him to jump into the glow. It is a short leap into the unknown, but Johnny takes a deep breath and steps forward. The blaze of colour completely embraces the fourteen year old. There is a warm and tingling sensation at the same time.

'Father where are we?'

We are in the heart of your soul.

'It is spectacular.'

Just like you Johnny. Pure, beautiful, full of Greatness and from the heart of God.

Johnny stands with his mouth wide open, speechless as he can find no words to express his thoughts. Finally he expresses one word to embrace all others.

'Awesome.'

A fine word Johnny, indeed you are.

'Me?'

You!

Johnny takes a big breath, and holds up his hands in surrender to God's answer.

Johnny, be strong, love yourself and love others as I love you. Now come here and give me a hug. You see hugging isn't so bad after all. Allow yourself to be immersed by my love Johnny.

Johnny falls into the embrace and melts as it overcomes his fear of touch. His being ignites as the feeling connects with every sinew in the young man's body.

Breathe it in Johnny.

Tears start to flow, the sensation completely overwhelming him, but at the same time exhilarating the senses.

'My Lord and my God.'

Remember Johnny the next time there is an opportunity to show your love and you find it hard to do so, think back on this moment and share it. I will be with you to help you love.

Then the Father hands Johnny an orange ribbon which he ties onto the second button of his pyjamas. They both turn silently and God leads Johnny to an exit that only He can see.

Chapter Five

Yellow

Johnny takes a deep breath on emerging from the orange glow.

'That was so powerful Father, I feel dizzy with euphoria. I just need to sit a moment to get my mind around what has just happened. What did just happen?'

'I hugged you Johnny.

'Wow that was some hug.'

You know young man, your mum wants to hug you. She wants to be able to come close to you in the same way you allowed me to embrace you. Do you think that you can allow her to do that, to shed your armour for a moment to have that intimacy with her?

'I would like to try.'

Then that is an amazing beginning Johnny.

Johnny takes another deep breath.

You look like you need a drink son. I will go and get you one.

God leaves the hallway and Johnny sits quietly on his own. His mind pondering on the two doors he has journeyed through. He suddenly becomes aware that another young man is sitting almost stock still on a chair opposite the Yellow door. The face of the owner is turned away so that Johnny cannot see who the lad is. As if aware that he is being looked at the other teenager turns towards Johnny, his face is masked, and nothing is spoken between the two. The silence seems very heavy and to lighten its mood Johnny decides to say 'hello'.

He cannot talk Johnny. God declares as he hands a tumbler of grapefruit juice to his student.

'What is wrong with him?'

Only he can reveal his story Johnny.

'But if he can't talk?'

In the beginning he chose not to talk, he was given the choice and he chose not to, and now he can't.

'That is really sad, why would you choose not to talk?'

Surrender is a hard thing to do Johnny.

'Are you talking of surrendering your speech, the joy of talking and of communicating?'

As I said, only he can tell you his story and only you can free him to do so.

'Me Lord?'

Yes, you Johnny.

Johnny takes a sip of the grapefruit juice which tastes bitter but as he has been given it by God, Johnny drinks it all and thanks his Teacher for the refreshment.

The three of us are going to explore what is behind the Yellow Door.

God looks at the other young man.

Are you ready?

There is a nod and the threesome walk towards the next colour of the rainbow.

As Johnny ventures through the door he is greeted with a vast expanse of yellow desert. The air is hot and sticky, and the sun blazes relentlessly at its highest point. There are people milling about complaining at the endless sand dunes and lack of fresh food and water.

'Is that Moses amongst the people Father?'

Well spotted Johnny.

'Why are they giving Moses a hard time?'

Because they are disgruntled with me, with the food I have given them. They are remembering the tasty food they had in Egypt, (See Numbers 11 v 4-6) but they are forgetting that in Egypt they were slaves. Here in the desert they are free, but having Manna porridge, Manna stew, Manna biscuits, Manna cakes, Manna pizza, Manna waffles, Manna burgers, Manna kebabs, Barbeque Manna to name a few dishes they are getting fed up and Moses, being their leader, is getting it in the neck.

'So he isn't very popular at the moment.'

That's right Johnny, he isn't very popular, he is doing my will and he isn't very popular.

'A bit like me?'

You are popular to me Johnny and that is all that matters!

'But it would still be nice to be popular.'

Being popular has limitations Johnny. You have to prove your worth to false people, and this can sometimes be at the expense of true friendships. But in order to be a leader like Moses, being popular was not on the agenda. As he couldn't please all of the people all of the time, he had to make difficult decisions in following my way and not the peoples' way. By the nature of his leadership he would become unpopular. Being a leader took him through his own personal wilderness.

'I know what that kind of desert is like Father.'

Indeed you do Johnny.

'So how does Moses deal with the unhappy hoards?'

'He cries to me and I advise him to get some help.' (See Numbers 11 v 16-17) **I am your help Johnny along with your family and those that you choose to invite into your world. Because it is not good for you to be alone. Moses at this point not only needs support from others, but he needs support for his mental wellbeing. Listen to his prayer Johnny.'**

'The load is far too heavy! If this is how you intend to treat me, just go ahead and kill me. Do me a favour and spare me this misery!' (See Numbers 11 v 15)

'Lord, Moses felt like me. That there was too much to bear. That he would be better off dead than trying to cope with a task or in my case a personality flaw that is too huge to carry.'

Indeed you are united with a hero.

'Wow, I never thought of it like that. Moses and me being the same. Cool.'

And he didn't give up Johnny.

'Why not if it was such a terrible burden?'

Because I reminded him of my power. (See Numbers 11 v 23) **That My Word always comes true. That I never give up and I will always be with him as I always will be with you. Nothing ever is impossible not for me.**

'And Moses believed you?'

Not at first. Moses forgot what I had done to free my people; I needed to remind him of the miracles I had worked to get them their freedom. How quickly man forgets!

234

'We must really put you to the test sometimes Lord.'

Um, indeed and it did make me angry and I took care of the situation. (See Numbers 11 v 33-34) **You see Johnny, I am the Maker of all and therefore only I can judge a situation and decide on the sentence, not man. I give and I take away.**

'What a responsibility Lord.'

Yes it is and too great a responsibility for mankind. Moses was a great leader Johnny. He made mistakes, doubted me, found being in charge hard and challenging, but he allowed me to use him for my purposes. He opened his life to my Holy Spirit. Moses is about Victory, about imitating Me. The Yellow Room is about my victory in your life about you imitating Me. Like Moses there will be times when things get hairy, but Johnny I am the Glory. I am the Glorious Divine Good. I am the Father to the fatherless. I place lonely people in families, and I set prisoners free and give them joy. (See Psalm 68) **I am the Victory.**

'How you understand me Father. You have placed me, a lonely person in a family, you want to set me free from my prison, and you want me to stretch out and embrace your Victory. I don't know what to say, I don't deserve all of this.'

But my son you do. Let me introduce you to the third member of our group.

The young man who had up to now just stood in the God's shadow appeared by the Father's side.

Take off your mask.

He did as he was commanded to do and a face looked at Johnny, yellow in appearance and sickening by the moment.

I would like to tell you who this is, but I can't. Only you have the key to release this poor soul.

235

'Will you tell me your story?' Johnny asks, tears welling up in his eyes as the disfigured teen slumps onto the sand. Johnny sits next to him and tries to look away but is compelled to retain eye contact.

With all his might the jaundiced boy tries to open his mouth but it is so welded together that nothing moves. Johnny looks around to see what they could use to help overcome this problem. His gaze falls on a stick which he gets up and fetches. He hands it to the fellow and as the hand stretches towards the piece of wood, Johnny is aware of the twisted digits that try desperately to grasp the implement. In the sand slowly and painfully the teenager writes:

'*You hate me.*'

'Hang on, how can I hate you when I don't know who you are.'

'*Everything about me you dislike.*'

'I don't understand.'

'*When you look at me you turn away.*'

'But I have never seen you before.'

'*You see me every day.*'

'What, when?'

The conversation falters and Johnny stares at God. 'What is he going on about Father?'

He has not finished Johnny; look closely into his eyes as they are the window to his soul.

'But all I can see is pain, rejection, sadness, loneliness, confusion and anger.'

'*I am a mirror.*'

'Pardon?'

'*You do not see the reflection?*'

'No.'

'*I am you.*'

Johnny's mouth drops as he suddenly understands. 'Oh Father I am so sorry, I have not honoured your creation, I have prayed against being different, longed to be free from my prison and regretted the day I was born. I have not embraced your love for me, for who I really am. I have drunk of the gall of bitterness and not listened to the truth, to Your Truth. Forgive me, forgive my blinkered vision.'

Johnny moves towards the disfigured young man and hugs him till the tears stream down from his eyes.

'I am sorry. I am so sorry.'

As they part the sickness slowly evaporates and Johnny sees a figure in brilliant light. Beyond the transformed image there is a waterfall.

Walk into the downpour of my love and be healed Johnny.

Together the boys move towards the cascading water and stand arms outstretched towards Heaven fully embracing the Spirits healing power. As Johnny steps forward from the waterfall he is alone, his body tingling with refreshment and power, his face alight with peace and surrender. He kneels before Jesus.

'My Lord and My God.'

My son, my beloved son, thank you for making the right choice, for choosing life over death. My spirit can now grow in you as you have accepted who you are, who I have made. You do not need to hide anymore in your room. In your weakness my power is made perfect and my grace is sufficient for you to walk tall as you are.

God takes Johnny by the hands and lifts him to a standing position. He hugs his son and Johnny returns the embrace with the knowledge that he is worthy of this encounter.

You no longer need to dwell in the desert Johnny. My promised land is awaiting you as you journey in My glow and radiate My glory through the love of My Holy Spirit.

The Father then hands Johnny a yellow ribbon which the teenager ties onto the third button hole of his pyjamas.

Chapter Six

Green

Back in the hallway Johnny looks at his ribbons and asks God why he has given them to him.

They will be a reminder of this night, of the journey you have begun with your new understanding and My Love.

Are you ready for the next door, the Green revelation?

Johnny smiles, 'I love green, it is nature's colour of health after an outpouring of rain. It's as though the trees and grass are praising God in joy, their branches and blades reaching up to the Heavens in adoration.

Then let's go and discover the lesson of nature.

Once on the other side of the green door, Johnny sees angels with their arms raised, singing and dancing among God's flora and fauna. The trees are emerald, sparkling with colours splashing off them in all directions. All manner of colours of green, jade, viridian, sap green, olive green, teal, asparagus, harlequin, and countless more. Their roots submerged in rich fertile earth, and their branches spreading out and culminating in leaves sparkling majestically as they sway lightly in the warmth of a gentle breeze that emanates from the Sun.

'Are we back in the Garden of Eden Father?'

No we are in your Garden.

Not for the first time Johnny stands looking confused. 'My garden?'

Indeed. In every one of my soul creations there is a garden which I tend. I am The Gardener. As much as I am your Creator I am also your Gardener. I tend to your needs, water you when you

grow dry, feed you with nourishment, comfort you when you wither and give you new life when you die. I cause your garden to overflow and enrich it bountifully by pruning and cultivating it. However, I also give you the choice to accept me as your gardener, as I do not tend any gardens without permission of the soul. Those souls that I do not sustain take their sustenance from the world; their gardens are overgrown and full of weeds. Sickness stunts their growth and damages any new shoots. And I weep as I did in the Garden of Gethsemane for these lost soul gardens.

'So what happens to these gardens, the ones that look to the world to look after their needs? Do you just leave them to die?'

Look around you Johnny, what do you see?

'Your creation Lord. Your beautiful work.'

Creation is my witness to my works Johnny, I have revealed my hand, (see Romans 1 v 18-20) **but even so, many remain unconvinced by My Grace and Faithfulness in the love I have for my creation. Their gardens wilt and die unless they turn to me for maintenance and care. I have painted a canvas for all to admire and see externally my authorship that is stamped everywhere.** (See Proverbs 8 v 22-31) **And man continues to question. I have also built your very being on firm foundations, but man is stubborn and blind to even see this. You are a scientist in the making Johnny. You like evidence to prove beyond reasonable doubt that I AM. Here is your evidence.**

'What is it Lord?'

It is proof that I AM your Maker. When you awake put this slide under your microscope and see your inheritance. It will reveal my Glory, my Holy Seed, my journey from the Beginning of time to the Resurrection and beyond. For those that believe this evidence their gardens shall want for nothing. For those that denounce even this truth, who believe in the creature rather than the Creator, nature will refine through its sowing and reaping. I AM merciful Johnny, I have used nature to illustrate lessons of life, I

will tend to my gardens for as long as the world exists, and man will continue to deny or accept my deliverance depending on who their soul follows. Faith and science go hand in hand because I created both. It is man's blindness that causes them to be separate and at odds with each other. Does not nature make you want to sing and worship, to raise your arms up in awe just as the angels are doing right now?

'Oh yes Father, without a doubt. Just like the flowers turn to the sun for warmth and the trees reach up to the skies to embrace you. Everything in nature that can, looks upwards, because that is where new life comes from. Birds drop seeds from the air which land and grow and produce more seeds that the wind blows and scatters in harvest time.'

As Johnny is talking the Angels start to sing, "Let all I am praise the Lord. O Lord my God, how great you are!"

They are singing psalm 104 Johnny; perhaps you might look it up when you have time.

'Their singing is to beautiful, can I just sit and listen to it?'

Of course my son, we have plenty of time. Would you like to hear it through my ears?

'That would be amazing.'

God opened Johnny's ears and his eyes and face lit up in a radiant glow.

As he adjusted to the music he looked around him and began to hear other things join in.

'Where are the other tones coming from Father?'

The grass, the trees, the inhabitants of the earth, the sea and everything within it, the sky and all that occupies its vastness, the stars, the universe, from every living creation. Everything pulsates in song to the glory of God. This is my orchestra.

241

'It's divine!'

Absolutely, and you are the first human to hear it perform. Johnny I want to reveal to you remarkable secrets both those seen and heard with the human eye and ear, but also those with the microscopic and telescopic eye. But even those will still be lacking in seeing the fullness of the Almighty.

'Lord, you favour me so highly, why?'

Because you already have a seeing eye, a brain that thinks differently, that solves problems in a unique way, who else would I choose; you are perfect for this mission?

'I am?'

You are. You really are! No one else can do it but you! I made you for this purpose.

'All along you knew my purpose and I thought you had rejected me because I am different.'

I never reject difference Johnny. Will you take up my challenge?

'How could I refuse my God. Yes, absolutely Yes.'

I love you my son, take your green ribbon now and put the slide into your top pocket so that you do not lose it.

'I love you too My Lord and My God. Thank you.'

As the Father and his son walk to the green door, Johnny notices something that is out of the order of the nature of the garden.

'Lord, what is that black plant?'

Ah, well spotted Johnny, I need to remove that.

The Gardener pulls at the plant and entrusts it to one of his angels.

Raphael, take this and dispose of it please, it does not belong in Johnny's garden.

God puts his hands on the teenager's shoulders and looks deeply into his eyes.

That Johnny was the plant of bitterness. Now as you have chosen to forgive and accept my healing in the matters that have caused you pain and anger, the plant can no longer live in your garden and has died from lack of nourishment. You have starved it of angry thoughts, jealous moments, wishing bad things would happen to others who have hurt you and wanting cruel justice and revenge over forgiveness.

'When Lord, did I make that decision?'

When you called for my help, and I saw your mother's heart as she prayed for you after she had read your letter that shared your inner most anguish. I am succour for a mum's tears, when they pray for their children. I never turn away when a mum surrenders her offspring to me.

Johnny sighs and tears appear in his eyes. He feels a thumb wipe away one that is edging its way down his cheek. The tear is captured in a small clear tumbler and a lid placed on top. God puts a label on the container and hands it to Johnny. He looks at it and reads the citation: A Jewel in the Sponge.

Johnny laughs. 'I like that Father.'

That's what you are my beautiful son. And when you raise this little jewel up to the light of the sun you will see my glory shining through your tear, the tear of a Sponge, Johnny Sponge.

In that moment the door opens and the two step through it and the glorious garden becomes a memory attached to the green ribbon.

Chapter Seven

Blue

The fifth door, the blue door, stands ajar. Johnny looks at it and frowns.

'Why is the door already open Father?'

Because God is calling us to wait on him, he wants us to urgently seek Him out.

'But I am not ready, I am not holy enough, I am not worthy to see Him. Father, I can't.'

That is true Johnny but God's Righteousness cannot wait. He has called us. He has left his door open for us to enter.

Johnny reached out to restrain the Father by pulling his arm back.

'Please Lord, I really can't.'

Johnny this is not down to your performance so far, it is by God's Grace and Righteousness that you are being called. Trust Me.

Reluctantly Johnny takes his hand off the Guide's arm and walks slowly towards the opening. As he enters the room he can hear nothing, and the only piece of furniture is a Judge's bench, standing empty awaiting its occupant. A voice penetrates the silence.

'All rise for the Judge.'

Johnny stands and looks around him, but nobody appears. He looks at his Master and enquires, 'Where is he?'

Where is who Johnny?

'The Judge?'

'Shhh the trial is about to begin.'

'What trial?'

Out of nowhere a woman half sits, half lays in the centre of the room. (John 8 v 1-11) It appears to be early morning. Men are standing around her, pointing fingers at her and accusing loudly that the woman has committed adultery. She looks frightened and bares signs of not having slept well due to having been incarcerated after her arrest the previous evening. Now she looks upon the crowd of men with fear, knowing that their judgement will condemn her to death.

'Where is the man who she is supposed to have committed adultery with?' Johnny asked. 'Why is he not there beside her?'

You are seeing a biased trial Johnny; this woman is carrying both their sins on her shoulders.

'But how is that fair?'

It isn't. Remember this is man's judgement.

Johnny suddenly remembers the story, and his eyes light up.

'But man's judgement was dismissed because no one could say that they had not sinned and she was free to go.'

That is correct Johnny, but she was told not to sin again. She was shown mercy and compassion with an obligation to not sin again as her road to freedom. This is God's Righteousness. Man on his own cannot become perfect, nor enter the Kingdom of God without an invitation. It is by God's calling alone, his Righteousness and Perfection that allows man to enter into his presence. A presence that is ever present, each moment of the day and night in your world. That is why the blue door was open, that is why the judge's seat was vacant, because God is always present to you. He is not there to judge with man's eyes but to invite you to His Righteous Justice.

245

'So God wants us to have an open mind?'

And an open Heart and Soul. Remember Matthew 5 v 3-10? God blesses all those that man thinks are weak, poor, distressed, starving, persecuted to name a few virtues that God loves and man believes are a sign of weakness.

'Father, you said earlier, **God is calling us to wait on him, he wants us to urgently seek Him out.** What did you mean by that?'

If you allow man's justice to rule your life then God's Will for you will be hidden by the clouds of everyday comments. God wants you to seek Him out in everything you do, right down to the boring, mundane chores of life to the miraculous that he can and will perform if you wait on Him. This is what the Blue Room offers you'

'But how do I do that? I am meant to follow rules and regulations that my parents, school and society tell me to. If I go and rob a bank and am caught, I shall be punished. I don't think a judge would let me say that God has forgiven me so you should too and let me go.'

No you are right Johnny. You do have to obey the rules of the land. That is why God has given you a blue-print, the Ten Commandments. This is because God is Righteous in All His dealings with men. (See Romans 3 v 22, Romans 4 v 13, Romans 5 v 17, Romans 9 v 30, 2 Corinthians 5 v 21, Phil 3 v 8-9) **But only through His Son can you be saved and made right with God. The woman who faced her jury was already guilty in their minds, but not in God's as she was worthy to be saved.**

A light shone on the woman again, she was surrounded by women, all asking her what had happened. She exclaimed excitedly, 'You see that man,' pointing to a stranger, 'he said that only the person who has never sinned should throw the first stone. Everyone walked away. There was no one left apart from the stranger and he asked where all my accusers were. I couldn't answer, so he declared that I was free to go but that I must not sin anymore.'

246

An onlooker asked if the woman was going to do as she was told.

'I have been forgiven and given a second chance, the man's eyes revealed to me His love, how can I refuse his invitation. From now on I shall thank God for his mercy and lead a good life. I have been soaked and washed clean, now I can move on with my life. I shall be forever thankful.'

The scene fades and Johnny turns to the man beside him. He studies him for a moment and sees the same love that the accused woman had seen in His eyes.

'Thank you Father.'

Now you too can move on Johnny.

'How my Lord?'

Each day if you wait on God every morning, saying Yes to His Will before you get up, your day will be in His Care. At night when you say thank you, God will bless you for seeking him no matter what has happened during the day. This can only happen because of the River of God that flows from His Kingdom. (See Revelation 22 v 1). **The Son left Heaven and lived on the earth so that the healing waters of God's Love could be made accessible to man. This is what the woman understood when she said that she could now move on with her life. She was thankful for God's Mercy and Justice and she knew that the only way forward now was to fix her eyes on God. She understood that she had to let go of her past and accept wholeness and healing with a thankful heart.**

The Blue Room door opened in front of them and Johnny knew that the lesson was over. There was a lot to think about, almost too much.

Johnny the blue ribbon is to remind you to move on from any hurts of the day and to thank God for his mercy and justice. In this way God's grace can flow through you and heal the pain. So by being thankful for each situation, healing and restoration will

flow through you instead of anger and bitterness. No longer will you feel desperate, different or lonely.

'Oh Lord, thank you, I wish I could provide the words that were big enough to speak of your awesomeness. I feel overwhelmed, kneeling is not enough. How can I show my gratitude?'

Thank you, spoken with a truthful heart, is big enough.

Johnny cannot overcome the powerful force to kneel; he bows his head and stretches out his arms, 'My Lord and my God, thank you.'

The Father bends down and hugs Johnny.

Because you are worth it.

Chapter Eight

Indigo

Johnny took a step back from the Guide's arms.

'Father, I think I have had enough for the moment, what you have shown me has blown my mind. I am not sure that I can absorb anymore.'

Time is of no consequence here Johnny; feel free to just inhale the peace around you.

As Johnny sat his fingers felt the soft fabric of the ribbons, each caught a shimmer of the light that was coming from the Indigo doorway. Johnny stood up feeling compelled to turn the handle of the next door, his overwhelming desire to just sit had gone almost as soon as he had experienced it. It was an odd feeling, one that he couldn't explain.

Inside the room Johnny's eyes grew wide, he was literally in the midst of a great storm and although the gushing waves of the sea and the winds beat down on a monstrous boat above him, he was still dry. Father and son ascended to the top of the commotion. There in every direction was water whether it was from above or below. Everything was covered in a film of liquid. Slowly the storm died down and then the scene sped up, a raven flew past and then returned. Then day became night, and night became day, and a dove was released from the enormous vessel. When it came back with a fresh olive leaf the waters were receding fast. When the waters had dried up enough a man removed the covering from the Ark and looked out. The scene was one of total devastation. And onto this land Noah stepped to begin life again. (See Genesis 7-8). High in the sky a pattern of colour shaped in a semi-circle hung surrounding the horizon.

The Master was the first one to speak.

'Never again, never again,' he spoke quietly.

249

From a distance Johnny could hear a voice, booming load and clear.

This sign is my covenant to you and to all ages, it is an eternal covenant. (See Genesis 9 v 8-17)

'Why Father?' Johnny exclaimed.

Man would not listen, so the earth was covered with water to cleanse it. But the cost was enormous so a covenant was declared between God and man. The rainbow was and still is the reminder that no matter how sinful man is, God will never again flood the earth to near extinction. The next covering would be God's own Son.

'Wow, that's some God.'

Yes indeed, He is some God. Come I want to show you the extent of this act.

They arose and journeyed upward to a City of Gold and jewels, colours that had never been seen before decorated the vision. A King was sitting on a thrown and his Son kneeling before him.

You see how the Son prostrates himself before the King. He has just been given his choice. He does not hesitate, but accepts his commission to cover the earth with his sacrifice. (See Phil 2 v 6-8) **You see all of this glory, this Heavenly place, that envelopes you in total peace and joy, the Son is leaving this to die for you and all mankind. His time on earth will be cruel and he will be treated as a criminal and nailed to a cross. The Son knows that and still he says Yes to His King. He will leave his royal robes and princely title and become a vulnerable baby, frail and at the mercy of mankind. But you know that the story does not end there because on his return to his King he is clothed anew** (See Phil 2 v 9-11) **and the Gates of Heaven opened to all of creation. And now mankind has a choice. Which garment will he cover himself in, which garment will you cover yourself in Johnny? The garment of the world** (See John 10 v 24-26) **or God's design** (See John 10 v 27-30)**?**

Johnny looks at the Son, he is smiling even though he knows his future, because he trusts His Father the King. For Him there is no contest, His Almighty God is to be obeyed and joyfully so, because of the Love that is ever present for Creation.

'But I am no saviour of the world Father,' Johnny confided, 'I am just me.'

Just you will do, but in my eyes you are not just you. You are a son of the Most High, an heir to God's Kingdom. Remember that when you look at the Indigo ribbon. You will never be just you. You have great worth.

Johnny took a deep breath, 'You are right, God made me and he didn't make rubbish. I am a sinner but I am worthy because he sent his Son to die for me, and if I deny that great sacrifice and think of myself as not worth it, then I deny Him. How can I deny my Saviour?

I am so proud of you Johnny, many adults can't grasp that concept and you within a night have uncovered a great secret.

'What's that saying? Oh yes, I know my own and my own know me.'

Exactly, my son.

Chapter Nine

Violet/Purple

Back in the corridor of the doors the Master turns to Johnny.

Before you go into the next room I need to give you something.

A cloak of purple in exquisite fine linen is placed around Johnny and fastened with a diamond clasp.

Now you are ready.

The two companions open the Violet door. On entering there is a huge welcoming roar, from a table full of people Johnny knows, all are dressed in purple linen. The room is decorated for a great celebration, with balloons, and streamers cascading triumphantly down from jewelled chandeliers. The table itself is full of sumptuous food fit for a king.

'Wow, what are we celebrating Lord?'

You.

'Me? I am not sure that I understand.'

This is your party; it has been prepared in your honour. Please take a seat at the table.

Johnny sees that there are two chairs, one of plain white wood polished to a mirror sheen and the other a great throne embedded with jewels. The young man makes his way to the white chair.

No my son, you are heading for the wrong seat, this one is for you.

The Master indicated the beautiful throne.

'But surely that is for you Father?'

This is your celebratory meal Johnny, it is only right that you sit in the seat of honour.

'But -!'

Remember what you have learnt?

'That I am worthy.'

Precisely, Johnny.

A gentle smile crosses the face of the One who loves Johnny. He escorts his student to his place at the table. Once seated Johnny watches the Humble Servant as He walks to the white chair and sits down.

What a joyous moment this is; eat, enjoy, break bread together, laugh, be at peace for I love your company, I love you all.

Johnny becomes totally immersed in the party, his joy evident and infectious. His earthy disabilities are non-existent as everything flows naturally from him. When all the food is eaten and the conversation nearing an end, the Host stands up, carries his chair and sits next to Johnny. There is a hush from the assembled.

Have you enjoyed your celebration, my son?

'It has been wonderful, thank you Father. I feel very honoured.'

Then Johnny remember this lesson. Today you have been among family and friends. Among people who can return favours to you. One day when you are in a position to invite others to your table, offer first the seats to those who cannot repay you. Who are unable to give you anything in return. (See Luke 14 v 12-14) **Then your reward will be in Heaven, where the righteous are clothed in Royal Garments.**

This struck a chord within Johnny.

'You mean even people like me, who are seen as different, who are bullied and ostracised because they don't fit into the same mould as everyone else?'

Yes Johnny. In fact anyone who the world sees as unclean, and not socially acceptable by the rules of the day. My table is always free to those that are treated unjustly. Do you understand my plan for you now, why you are special to me, why I need you?

'You need me Lord?' An incredulous expression formed on the young man's face.

Johnny, you are my face, my hands, my heart, and my love. It is through My people that I am able to meet with those who need me. I have called you, inadequate as you think you are, You are my choice.

A deep breath comes from Johnny's lungs, a sudden realisation that only he will do. God is calling him. God is calling him, Johnny Sponge, the laughing stock of school, the person everyone thinks is odd, strange, different, a joke.

Only you will do Johnny, you were created for this.

'But...'

Still buts Johnny? Look at who I called to hand over the keys of the kingdom to. Peter, a fisherman who denied me three times. He was no scholar, but I knew he would be a great fisher of men. Then there was Paul who persecuted the Christians, and was a murderer. His repentance and exhaustive example to bring the news of mercy and salvation turned countless non-believers to God. (See Ephesians 3) **But they did not do these things on their own, Johnny. The mighty Power of God within them, accomplished these tasks. That is why you can succeed, because a Holier Spirit will lead you on your journey from now on. He will give you the strength, determination and the key to be fruitful in**

254

this commission.

'Once again you ask a lot Lord. But I know that I will not find rest until I accept your will for me.'

You are a wise young man.

'I have an awesome Teacher.'

I think you are ready Johnny.

The other members of the celebration have drifted away now and it is just Johnny and his Guide sitting in the Violet Room. Johnny is handed his ribbon and he ties it on the last button left on his pyjamas.

There is one last place for you to visit.

'Another room, I thought there were only seven.

There are, but this place is made up of all the colours put together. Come let me show you.

Chapter Ten

White

As Johnny leaves the Violet Room all of the other doors merge to form one larger bright white expanse.

This place Johnny has neither beginning nor end, it just is. Together we shall walk into the white light.

The brightness to human eyes is capable of destroying the retinas of the eyes, but Johnny feels no discomfort. He looks at where his body should be and sees only light. From this glorious state, words from the Bible flow through Johnny. From beginning to end all things begin to make sense, from Creation to Revelation, nothing confuses Johnny anymore. All of his questions are answered in a flash, even before he knows what to ask.

Peace filters through the light, everything just is.

Chapter 11

The slide

The alarm goes off waking Johnny to a new day. He opens his eyes and sees his room bathed in light from the rising sun. He immediately pulls off the duvet to look at his pyjamas. There in each button hole is a colour from the rainbow.

'It really happened!' he yells, 'It really happened!'

He reaches into his jacket pocket and finds the slide. Johnny fumbles around to find his glasses, pushing things out of the way in an attempt to locate them. Then he handles something familiar. In an instant he has donned glasses and is sitting at his microscope with the slide in place. 'Evidence, irrefutable evidence from the Green Room,' he whispers. He feels himself shaking knowing that he is on the brink of an amazing discovery. The words spoken in the Green Room come to him.

When you awake put this slide under your microscope and see your inheritance. It will reveal my Glory, my Holy Seed, my journey from the Beginning of time to the Resurrection and beyond.

It is time, Johnny decides, and he bends over and looks through the powerful lenses at the answer....

Epilogue

Here is the ending of this book taken from 'How to make Victoria Sponge' Chapter Four.

Henry enquires how Johnny is, and suddenly I wonder too, then from the kitchen my son appears, all dressed in his uniform and ready to leave.

'I want to go to school,' he announces as he passes me by, looking straight at Henry and telling him to hurry up.

'He's fine,' I say.

About the author

Margaret Kazmierczak lives in the South West of England with her husband Peter and three children along with their cat who is the mistress of the house.

Margaret's varied life experiences have helped her in creating *How to make Victoria Sponge*. Faith has always been important. Having a personal relationship with God has provided that inner strength to help with whatever life has thrown at her.

Margaret describes herself as a middle aged teenager, with a wicked sense of humour. She loves 'people watching' and finds inspiration in the challenges of everyday life. Her belief that nothing is impossible has got her into many sticky situations, but without this conviction *How to make Victoria Sponge* would never have been written.

Having left school with no qualifications as the term 'dyslexia' had not been coined back in the dark ages, Margaret embarked on a journey of self discovery. This took her into the WRAF, an enclosed religious order, the NHS, college, business and finally education. She fitted in married life and looking after her elderly father-in-law along the way.

When asked if she has learnt anything about life during her travels, she comments, 'Not really, but I have learnt from its mistakes. It is the getting up that brings growth and understanding.' Margaret's advice to others is, 'Never underestimate your potential.'